Cook Well, Stay Well
with Parkinson's Disease

Super Foods for Super People

Kathrynne Holden, MS, RD

*****

A portion of the proceeds
from the sale of this book
will be donated to help fund research
into a cure for Parkinson's disease

Cook Well, Stay Well
with Parkinson's Disese

Super Foods for Super People

Kathrynne Holden, MS, RD

Published by:

Five Star Living, Inc.
Fort Collins, Colorado 80524

Copyright 2003
by Five Star Living, Inc.
ISBN 0-9664370-1-2

Printed in the United States of America.

For information, or to order books, call or write:

Five Star Living, Inc.
760 S.E. Frontage Road
Fort Collins, Colorado 80524

Toll Free: 1-877-565-BOOK (2665)
Fax: 970-224-5099
sonjaj@1stclassdirect.com
Website: www.nutritionucanlivewith.com

Table of Contents

FOREWORD

People with PD must eat. But what to eat? and how to prepare it?

Why not a cookbook? There are cookbooks for heart disease. Cookbooks for diabetes. Why not a cookbook for PD?

But who could write it? Who would know enough about food, diets, nutrients and vitamins for people with PD? There is, in my opinion, only one person in the world.

Kathrynne Holden, moderator of "Ask the Parkinson Dietitian." The book should be, will be, on the shelf of everyone with PD, everyone who entertains someone with PD, everyone who wants to know what a person with PD should eat – and how it should be prepared.

Abraham Lieberman, M.D.
Medical Director
National Parkinson Foundation

A single brozil nut = day need of selinium
    selinium
cherries- with E
parsley- mild diuretic
Green tea- protects against cell death
hummis = good snack

PLEASE NOTE:

The material in this book is intended as general information. _It is not intended to provide medical services, nor medical nutrition therapy._ Readers are encouraged to seek personal medical advice from a health professional for their health needs.

PREFACE

In the years since I first wrote and published *Eat Well, Stay Well with Parkinson's Disease* (EWSW), many readers have called or written to say how much they benefitted from the book; and a common request was for "more recipes – please, more recipes."

I think this is because food is such an important part of our daily life. It's a part of social occasions – weddings, birthdays, holidays. It gives us pleasure and comfort. We share it with our loved ones. And it nourishes us. Perhaps more importantly, people with PD may have a greater need for some nutrients, to help fight the effects of the disease.

In EWSW, I discuss the many nutrition pitfalls that can occur with PD, and how to prevent nutrition-related diseases. EWSW has in-depth information on the numerous obstacles to staying healthy – nausea, acid reflux, appetite loss, bone thinning, constipation, need for B vitamins, slowed movement of the gastrointestinal tract, and more – and many people have written to tell me that the book has turned their lives around.

But *a cookbook* is important, too – in other ways. There are foods, herbs, and nutrients that are especially helpful for the particular concerns that often occur in PD – you might call them **PD superfoods**.

> PD superfoods are those that contain high amounts of vitamins, minerals, antioxidants, flavonoids, and other substances that are particularly needed by those with PD. Better still, foods contain these nutrients in the ideal proportions to support each other in the body, and in a balance that is ideal for our metabolism. Supplements may be needed as well, but food is the gold standard when it comes to nutrition.

This cookbook, therefore, focuses on what I think of as "super foods for Parkinson's" –

- high in antioxidants
- fiber-rich
- good sources of calcium, magnesium, B vitamins, protective fats, or other nutrients of concern in PD

Because I have friends with PD who love cooking, I've included some complex recipes; but, because many people with PD, and caregivers of those with PD, often don't have time to spend cooking, you'll find that most of the recipes are for "everyday" foods – not too complicated, but taste-appealing.

Do you have to eat only these recipes? No! Certainly not – you'll want to go out to restaurants, celebrate family occasions with traditional recipes, and have your old favorites. Consider "Cook Well" a starting point. Try to prepare a few of these recipes each week, for the nutrients, fiber, and protection they afford. Perhaps it will give you ideas for modifying some of your own favorite recipes. I hope you'll enjoy the recipes contained here as much as I've enjoyed writing this book.

Best regards,

Kathrynne Holden, MS, RD

QUESTIONS ?   E-MAIL ME !
If you have questions, you can e-mail me. Go to *The Parkinson Foundation* website:
http://www.parkinson.org/
Locate "Ask the Parkinson Dietitian." Click on that link and follow the directions to sign on to the forum. You can then send your questions, and I will respond.

ACKNOWLEDGMENTS

I wish to thank *The Parkinson Foundation*, and Dr. Lieberman in particular, for providing the forum "Ask the Parkinson Dietitian." It allows me to e-mail individual nutrition help to people with PD and their families around the world.

Special thanks also to *Medtronic, Inc.*, for their generous sponsorship of "Ask the Parkinson Dietitian."

This book would not be possible without the help of my husband, Steve, and his endless patience and computer problem-solving.

For permission to reprint recipes, my thanks to:

Alaska Seafood Marketing Institute:
   http://www.state.ak.us/local/akpages/COMMERCE/asmihp.htm
Allrecipes.com: http:// www.Allrecipes.com
Ms. Betty Ann Carroll: Betty Ann Carroll's SuperBread
California Egg Commission: http://www.eggcom.com
California Seafood Council: http://www.ca-seafood.org/index.htm
Florida Department of Agriculture and Consumer Services:
   http://www.florida-agriculture.com
Idaho Potato Commission: http://www.famouspotatoes.org/
Indiana Soybean Board: http://www.soyfoods.com/index.html
Monitor Sugar: Internet address: http://www.monitorsugar.com/
Mushroom Council: http://www.mushroomcouncil.com/index.html
National Honey Board: http://www.honey.com/
National Pasta Association: Internet address: http://ilovepasta.org/
North American Blueberry Council: http://www.blueberry.org/
Ontario White Bean Producers:
http://users.imag.net/~lon.whitepeabeans/
Stash Tea: http://www.stashtea.com/
USA Rice Federation: http://www.ricecafe.com/

GETTING STARTED

Parkinson's and Food – What's the Connection?

Parkinson's disease (PD) is a highly stressful condition, and stress creates free radicals, which can lead to heart disease, cancers, and many other diseases. Free radicals are also implicated in the death of the dopamine-producing neurons, which brings about the PD symptoms. Foods rich in antioxidants help prevent free radical damage.

There are many different kinds of antioxidants – some are vitamins, others are minerals, still others go by the names of polyphenols, flavonoids, or isoflavones. Each antioxidant works in a different way, and in different areas of the body, and many work best when supported by other components of a particular food. That's why food is so much more valuable than vitamin pills – supplements just don't have the same nutrient balance.

Another concern is that PD can slow the action of the colon, causing constipation, bowel impaction, hemorrhoids, and raising risk for colorectal cancer. Foods high in fiber can both protect the colon against cancer and help with constipation.

Still another area of concern: PD medications can bring about unwanted side effects:

- Edema, a condition in which fluid is retained in the tissues, causing swelling, weight gain, and sometimes elevated blood pressure.

- Long-time use of levodopa can lead to elevated serum homocysteine, a substance in the blood that can increase risk for dementia, hardening of the arteries, and stroke. Homocysteine is cleared from the blood by B vitamins, and those with PD need to be careful to get plenty of foods rich in B vitamins.

- Nausea, appetite loss, and dry mouth, all of which can affect the amount and kinds of food eaten, sometimes leading to malnutrition.

Let's examine some of the foods used in *Cook Well* recipes that can help people with PD maintain top nutritional health.

Berries. Berries and cherries are rich in antioxidants. Blackberries, black raspberries, blueberries, strawberries, and cranberries are being studied for their health-protective properties. Preliminary findings indicate that blueberries may help protect the brain against Alzheimer-type dementia;[1] the antioxidant activity of a substance in cherries was found to be superior to vitamin E;[2] cranberries may help protect against urinary tract infection, and have been found to be rich in free-radical-scavenging antioxidants.[3]

Fish. There are so many good things to say about fish, it's hard to know where to start. It contains a high-quality protein, is rich in vitamin B12, low in cholesterol, and there are so many varieties of fish and seafood that almost everyone can find several favorites. It helps protect against heart disease, may help lower blood pressure and triglycerides, and may help alleviate the pain of rheumatoid arthritis.

Research is also focusing on a link between fish oil and depression.[4, 5] Over the years, western society has increasingly replaced fish with meats, and the rate of depression has risen. Researchers have found that the omega-3 fatty acids found in fish oil appear to be linked to better mental health. Why? The brain contains a high amount of omega-3 fatty acids – the same fatty acid found in fish oil. Without fish, it's difficult to get enough of this precious fatty acid in the diet, and the lack may be a factor in depression and other mental disorders. Studies indicate that some people who begin eating fish, or even consuming fish oil capsules, have seen an improvement in feelings of depression.[6]

> There is a high rate of depression among those with PD, and consuming fish several times a week may help. But even if it does not, fish is an excellent food for many other reasons.

What about mercury levels in fish? Long-lived and "predator" fish may contain methylmercury, which can harm the developing nervous system of an unborn child, if eaten regularly. Women of childbearing age and children under age six are advised to avoid shark, swordfish, tilefish, king mackerel and fresh caught or frozen tuna steaks. Regarding canned tuna, women of childbearing age can eat about one can per week (six ounces.) A woman who weighs less than 135 pounds should eat less than one can of tuna per week. Mercury may also harm the nervous systems in adults, although a connection between mercury and Parkinson's disease has not been demonstrated. For more information and updates, see the Environmental Protection Agency site: http://www.epa.gov/waterscience/fish/advisory.html

Flax seed. Flax seed is a rich source of fibers, both soluble and insoluble, and therefore can help with constipation[7] as well as lower cholesterol in the blood.[8] It contains more alpha-linolenic acid (an omega-3 essential fatty acid) than any other plant seed. It's also a source of lignans, which are being studied as a possible cancer-preventive agent.[9, 10] Flax seed must be ground in order to be used by the body; whole seeds will pass through the digestive system entire. It can be freshly ground in the blender or coffee grinder, then stored in the refrigerator or freezer for up to 30 days.

Ginger. This aromatic root (rhizome) has been used as food, herb, and medicine for thousands of years. Besides adding a spicy flavor to foods, it can help relieve nausea and motion sickness.

> Ginger promotes saliva, which may be helpful for the dry mouth so common with PD medications; it may also stimulate the appetite.[11]

You can use the fresh root, the dried, powdered form, or the crystallized (candied) form. Caution: ginger may act as a blood thinner. Persons who use coumadin, aspirin, or other blood-thinning agents should consult their physician before using ginger.

Grains. Whole grains, such as wheat, barley, rye, oats, and corn contain valuable bran, as well as vital trace minerals that are lost with refining and processing. Whole grains should be an important part of the daily diet.

Grapes / grape juice. Concord grape juice is a rich source of *flavonoids*, compounds that act as antioxidants; in a study, it was found to compare favorably with supplements of vitamin E, and also to contain a unique antioxidant potential even greater than supplements. The authors state, *"Concord grape juice flavonoids are potent antioxidants that may protect against oxidative stress and reduce the risk of free radical damage and chronic diseases."*[12] In other studies, a different compound in grapes, pterostilbene, was identified. This compound is believed to have both anti-cancer and anti-diabetes properties,[13] both potentially important for those with PD.

Honey. Honey is sweeter than sugar, and much more flavorful, making it a good choice for those with a "sweet tooth." But there's more to honey than its sweet flavor. Honey helps to heal skin injuries, including ulcers and burns, even killing antibiotic-resistant bacteria; it also helps to reduce scarring. And there's more – honey contains about the same amount of antioxidants as some fruits, including oranges and strawberries.[14] Choosing honey over sugar is better for your health.

Legumes. Legumes are dried beans, peas, and lentils. They are among the oldest of foods, used around the world for centuries. In the far East soybeans have been a dietary staple for hundreds of years -- in India, many kinds of lentils and split peas are used to make delicious, savory *dal* and other dishes; in the Bible, a story tells how Esau traded his birthright for "a mess of pottage," which was probably a lentil stew.

Legumes are an exceptional source of fiber, folate (a B vitamin), magnesium, protein, and complex carbohydrates. I recommend a serving of legumes daily or every other day.

Lemons. Lemons have more vitamin C than oranges, and also contain a small amount of calcium in a very well-absorbed form. Furthermore, they are a kind of internal antiseptic – they are antinflammatory, and have mild diuretic properties as well.[11]

Nuts. In EWSW, you'll find I recommend a combination of raw nuts, to be eaten daily. This is because nuts are such a valuable food for those with PD. They are a rich natural source of vitamin E, protective fatty acids, and hard-to-find trace minerals. One study found that people who ate foods rich in vitamin E were less likely to develop PD; supplements of vitamin E (pills) did not have any effect.[15]

> A single Brazil nut contains an entire day's recommended supply (55 mcg) of selenium, an important trace mineral that works together with vitamin E as an antioxidant.

Although the recipes here often use nuts in cooking, heating nuts destroys much of the vitamin E content, so try to eat some of them raw.

Oils. Vegetable oils are a little-known source of vitamin E. Again, however, cooking destroys most of the vitamin. Some oils, particularly sunflower and safflower oils, have very high amounts of vitamin E. They are too delicate to use for cooking, so purchase a small bottle, keep it in the refrigerator, and use it for the salads, smoothies, and other recipes that don't require heat. Olive and peanut oils can withstand a much higher heat, so use these for sauteing and baking.

Parsley. Parsley has been used traditionally as a mild diuretic, as well as to help counteract urinary tract infections and kidney stones. PD, and its medications, can lead to fluid retention (edema), and it's wise to avoid harsh diuretic medications if possible – try parsley instead. It's also a good source of vitamin C, and its chlorophyll content helps to counteract "garlic breath." Caution: a few people may be allergic to parsley; also pregnant women should avoid parsley.[11]

Prunes. Prunes (dried plums) have an exceptionally high antioxidant content. Further, they contain sorbitol, a natural laxative, making them a particularly good food for people with PD who experience constipation. They are also a good fiber source, and taste wonderful in baked goods. It's best to eat whole prunes, stewed or pureed, rather than prune juice, for their fiber and nutrients.

Sweet potato. These are high in fiber and a super source of vitamin A and carotenes, important antioxidants. But there's more: many people find that baked sweet potatoes help prevent constipation. The skins are a good fiber source, so if you like baked sweet potatoes, try to eat some of the skin.

Tea. Green, black, white, and oolong teas are receiving increasing interest among researchers for their possible health benefits. Teas contain polyphenols, compounds with powerful protective and antioxidant properties. In a preliminary study, black, green, and oolong forms were found to increase insulin activity,[16] important for those with diabetes; another study compared people who drank green tea vs. those who did not, finding that the green tea drinkers were 42% less likely to have a heart attack.[17]

Of importance to those with PD, another study suggests that long-term tea drinking may help protect against bone thinning.[18] Also, promising animal studies indicate that an extract of green tea could help prevent PD, and also help protect against cell death in those who have PD.[19]

Turmeric. This is an herb used for coloring, flavoring, and also as a medicine in India and China. It has been used to treat flatulence; poultices applied to the skin have been used to relieve pain and inflammation. However, current research is directed toward its antioxidant properties, and its possible use in fighting cancer,[20] diabetes,[21] and heart disease,[22] and in wound healing.[23] Of perhaps even greater interest are studies to determine whether it might be of use in preventing or treating Alzheimer-type dementia. Both cognitive impairment and sometimes dementia can occur in PD. Animal studies indicate that components of turmeric were protective against the oxidative stress implicated in Alzheimer's disease.[24] [25]

How to read and use the recipes

You'll quickly see that below each recipe there are three sections:
- What's great about this recipe?
- SuperSource
- Nutrition information per serving

What's great about this recipe ?

In this section, you'll see eight boxes, one or more of which will contain a check mark. This alerts you to special areas of importance, so that people with different needs can quickly see whether a recipe will match those needs. If you see an asterisk (*), look in the comments at the top of the page for tips or substitutions.

Easy-Fix – The recipe doesn't require complicated preparation; in some cases, long-cooking ingredients such as beans or rice can be cooked and frozen ahead of time – these recipes may also be labeled "Easy-Fix."

Quick-Fix – Can be prepared in 45 minutes or less, sometimes using ingredients you've prepared and frozen ahead of time.

Easy-Chew – Just what it sounds like – the food isn't difficult to chew. *Caution:* easy-chew does NOT mean it's easy to swallow. Persons with dysphagia (swallowing problems, choking) should see a speech pathologist. Dysphagia can be dangerous. If you have problems swallowing, or choking, ask your doctor for a referral to a speech pathologist.

Hands-on – Does it take a long time to finish a meal? Is it difficult to manipulate a fork, or cut up meat? "Hands-on" means these are foods that can be picked up and eaten with the hands, or sipped from a mug; they don't require the use of a fork, knife, or spoon.

Bone Health – It's important to pay special attention to bone health. These recipes contain at least 10% of the RDA for two or more of the following: calcium, magnesium, phosphorus, vitamin D, vitamin K.

Heart Health – These recipes are low in saturated fat and cholesterol; and/or contain omega-3 fatty acids or nuts; and/or contain at least 10% of the RDA for two or more of the following: vitamin E, selenium, B6, B12, folate, fiber.

Sweetie – Many, in fact most, folks with PD develop a craving for sweets. So I've included a number of recipes for desserts and sweet beverages. However, they all have a little something extra – antioxidant-rich fruits, a high-fiber ingredient, extra calcium – something that makes them special as well as sweet.

High fiber – These recipes contain at least 1.5 grams of fiber per 100 calories, or contain at least 25% of the daily goal amount (25 grams), making them a good fiber source. Fiber, along with plenty of fluid, can help manage constipation, and it also promotes heart health.

SuperSource

"SuperSource" means that nutrients named in this box are present in at least 25% of the daily goal amount for that nutrient. So, if you have been diagnosed with osteoporosis, for example, you can easily find recipes that are good sources of bone-strengthening nutrients. People with PD need to check for super sources of the B vitamins, also.

Nutrition information per serving

This tells you the calories; grams of protein, carbohydrate, fat, and saturated fat; and amounts of cholesterol, sodium, and fiber present in a serving. This is important for people who have diabetes and need to account for carbohydrates; for those who need to watch sodium, cholesterol and saturated fat; and also for those using levodopa, who may need to adjust protein amounts.

- When substitutions are suggested in the recipe, the nutrient analysis is given for the ingredients as listed, not for substitutions.
- In some cases, calories may not match the total grams of fat, carbohydrates, and protein shown; this may be due to the nutrient analysis software, or because I have rounded grams to the nearest whole figure.
- "Good source of" means that a serving contains at least 10% of the daily goal amount for that nutrient.

Tips for success

Now that we've examined "super foods" and learned how to read and use the recipes, let's take a look at some ways to make food preparation quicker and easier.

Invest in some time-saving appliances. You don't need expensive, top-of-the-line appliances to make any of these recipes. However:

- An inexpensive food processor will quickly and safely chop, slice, shred and puree foods, making your life much simpler.
- A blender will whip up nourishing shakes and smoothies, and puree soups and other cooked foods.
- A "slow cooker" or crockery cooker is like a little oven that can be left alone for hours while you work or shop; your meal is ready whenever you are.

- Another good investment is a small inexpensive kitchen scale. Measuring by weight is much more accurate than measuring by volume, and if grams of protein become a concern, weighing out an ounce or two of meat, fish, or cheese can make a world of difference in levodopa absorption.

Cook ahead and freeze. Many of the most beneficial foods for PD are whole, unprocessed foods, like brown rice and dried beans. When you know you'll be at home for a few hours, cook a large pot of, for example, barley. Then, after it's cool, measure it out into one-cup portions, and freeze these. Put each portion in a lock-top plastic bag; flatten the bags and stack them on top of each other, and place in the freezer. When you need to make a recipe that calls for barley, it will quickly thaw for your use. For cooking instructions, see "SIDE DISHES – grains, vegetables, fruits."

Miscellaneous:
- Buy ground flax seed and store in freezer, or grind your own in small batches, store in the refrigerator up to 30 days.
- For some people, cow's milk blocks the absorption of levodopa to a greater extent, and sometimes for a longer time, than other proteins. If milk is a problem for you, try one of the soy or rice milks instead. These can be substituted in most recipes.

How to use the <u>Menu Section</u>

In this section, you'll find complete, one-day menus. These are examples, or "templates," that you can use to design your own menus. They're planned to provide about 2000 - 2200 calories per day, which may be too much for some folks, too little for others; you'll need to adapt serving sizes to your own needs.

How to use the menus? Let's say you often experience constipation. Examine the menu called "High Fiber." You'll see that it uses a number of recipes selected for their high fiber content. It also demonstrates the need for plenty of fluids, to combat constipation. Now, you can go through the cookbook and locate recipes marked "High Fiber." Put together your own daily menus, with at least 25 grams of fiber per day.

> NOTE: At the bottom of each menu, you'll see a box marked "*Concerns*." Notice that the menus fall short in some nutrients. It's difficult to get all of the nutrients you need in a one-day menu. This is why it's a good idea to take a daily multivitamin supplement.

You'll also notice that very few recipes contain vitamin D. That's because it's not found in many foods: fatty fish, and fish liver oil contain moderate amounts, and fortified foods, such as milk and some breakfast cereals are good sources. Sunlight is also a good source, because sunlight on our skin causes it to produce vitamin D. However, during the winter months, and in northern areas especially, sunlight is too weak to produce this effect.

If you're not including fortified foods and fatty fish daily, and having regular exposure to sunlight, you'll need supplements of vitamin D. It's necessary for calcium absorption, to protect against bone thinning.

Reading the recipes. Although most people are quite familiar with kitchen measurements, here are some points to keep in mind when reading the recipes:

- Oven temperature is shown in degrees Fahrenheit (F.)
- 100 degrees Fahrenheit = 37.8 degree Celsius
- 100 degrees Celsius = 212 degrees Fahrenheit
- One tablespoon (US) = 3 teaspoons (US) = about 15 grams
- 1 teaspoon (US) = 1.07 teaspoon (UK)
- 1 coffee spoon (UK) = 0.25 teaspoon (US)
- 1 fluid ounce (US) = 6 teaspoons (US) = 2 tablespoons (US)
- 1 fluid ounce (US) = 1.04 fluid ounce (UK)
- One cup (US) = 8 fluid ounces (US) = 236.5milliliter/cc

Abbreviations
- pant. acid = pantothenic acid (a B vitamin)
- vit. = vitamin
- F. = Fahrenheit
- RDA = Recommended Dietary Allowance
- DRI = Dietary Reference Intake

Daily goal amounts for nutrients. Amounts of nutrients needed have been derived from the Dietary Reference Intakes (DRIs) for males age 50-70 years. They are within safe limits for all adults, both men and women, except for women who are pregnant or lactating. Children, and women who are pregnant or lactating, should consult a registered dietitian to determine their optimal intake of nutrients.

Recipes were analyzed using Nutritionist IV software (version 4.1, first quarter 1997, First Data Bank, San Bruno, CA).

SURGERY AND YOUR NUTRITIONAL HEALTH

As you probably know, there are excellent surgical options available for PD, used when medications no longer manage the symptoms. *Deep Brain Stimulation* has proved to lessen symptoms such as off-times, dyskinesia,[26] rigidity and tremor;[27] improve walking ability and balance;[28] and provide for better health and quality of life.[29,30,31] Besides that, many people find they can reduce the amount of PD medications needed.[32,33] This is very good news, because the less medications needed, the less chance of adverse side effects, such as dyskinesia, nausea, appetite loss, and dry mouth. Some people have reported that they aren't constipated as often, possibly because they are eating better.

If you are contemplating Deep Brain Stimulation surgery – or any other type of surgery – keep in mind that being in the best possible physical and mental health before _any_ surgery (or hospitalization for any other reason) is important. Studies have shown that poor nutritional health (malnutrition) can lengthen the hospital stay, and can also raise the risk for infections and even death.[34,35] On the other hand, being in good nutritional health could shorten your time in the hospital, as well as your recovery time.[36] It may even increase the likelihood that you'll be a good candidate for Deep Brain Stimulation surgery.

Good health means staying at a healthful weight (not losing, or gaining, too much weight); maintaining good muscle tone, handgrip strength, and bone density; and making sure at your annual checkup that all your laboratory reports are top-notch.

Will Deep Brain Stimulation surgery affect your nutritional health? It may, and probably for the better. As noted above, there are reports of decreased constipation; other patients say their nausea is lessened because they need fewer medications; others state their appetite is improved, or that they can hold and use forks and knives more efficiently. One study found that because dyskinesia was diminished, individuals were not burning as many calories in unwanted movements, thus they were able to regain weight they had lost,[37] highly important for those who have lost valuable muscle mass.

Deep Brain Stimulation surgery is a good option for many people with PD; if you think it might be important for you someday, be sure to protect your health, including nutritional health, starting now.

APPETEASERS AND SNACKS

Snacks are great! For parties, or just when someone drops by. I've chosen foods we sometimes don't think about as "snack food" – shrimp, nuts, mini-sandwiches, dips – foods that have special nutritional value for those with PD. Nuts have trace minerals not easily found in most foods; tiny sandwiches are easy to eat and don't fill you up too much. And they're also terrific party appetizers. But that's not all – snacks are also a delicious way to both gain – and LOSE – weight !

Need to gain weight? Adding some snacks can help. It's often easier to eat a few bites of food than a full meal, yet those bites add extra calories; and if your snack contains vegetables, fruit, fiber, and other nutrients, then you're fighting off disease as well.

Want to lose weight? Eating small meals, with a snack in between, can help curb the appetite while still keeping calories low. It's a funny thing, but our bodies seem to want to store calories from a large meal, yet are ready and willing to burn calories from several small meals – even though the day's calories add up to the same number!

Snacks also help keep a steady supply of blood sugar available. When blood sugar drops too low, you can feel tired, dizzy, sometimes irritable. A bit of food in between meals can help fight fatigue.

The snacks and appetizers here are chosen from a wide variety of sources – cookbooks on entertaining, websites, and my own family's favorites; however, I've selected them all with an eye to the nutrition needs of those with PD.

If you use levodopa and like to snack between meals, remember that if the snack contains protein, you need to be sure to take the levodopa about 30 minutes before the snack. Alternatively, choose snacks that contain no more than 2 grams of protein.

Rainy Day Tomato Snack
Servings: 2

A treat on sunny days, as well as rainy ones. Reprinted with permission of the Florida Tomato Committee.

1 slice bacon
1 1/3 medium ripe, firm, tomatoes, washed and cored

2 slices whole wheat bread
1/2 cup grated Mozzarella cheese

1. Preheat oven to 350 degrees, putting rack in the center of the oven.
2. Lay bacon in a baking pan and place pan in preheated oven; bake for 10 minutes, until crispy. Remove, and place pan on a heatproof surface to cool. When the bacon has cooled remove with a fork and place on paper towel to drain excess grease. When bacon is cool to the touch, crumble and set aside.
3. Meanwhile, on a cutting board cut the tomatoes into thick slices with a utility knife.
4. Place the slices of bread on a cookie sheet. Arrange two slices of tomato on each slice of bread, sprinkle bacon crumbs over the tomato and top with grated cheese.
5. Place cookie sheet in center of oven. Bake for about 7 minutes, until cheese melts. Remove from oven and transfer to a cutting board using a spatula. Cut each slice into thirds and serve.

What's great about this recipe ?

"Easy-Fix"	✔	"Bone Health"	✔
"Quick-Fix"	✔	"Heart Health"	
"Easy-Chew"		"Sweetie"	
"Hands-on"	✔	"High Fiber"	✔

SuperSource: Chromium, manganese, fiber

Nutrition information per serving: 180 calories, 17 g carbohydrates, 11 g protein, 9 g fat, 4 g saturated fat, 17 mg cholesterol, 354 mg sodium, 3 g fiber. Good source of vitamins A, B1, C, K, iron, calcium, phosphorus, copper.

Cheesy Nutty Triangles

Servings: 6

These little triangles are a nice party treat, as well as a tempting tidbit, and your food processor can do all the work of chopping and blending. There is some loss of vitamin E compared to raw nuts. Reprinted courtesy of Dundee Hazelnuts & The Oregon Hazelnut Industry.

2 tablespoons filberts (hazelnuts), chopped
1/4 cup grated Cheddar cheese
1 teaspoon fresh parsley, snipped; or 1/2 teaspoon dried parsley
1/4 teaspoon grated onion, or to taste

2 tablespoons mayonnaise
Dash (few drops) Worcestershire sauce
Dash cayenne pepper
3 slices thin whole wheat bread
1/2 tablespoon imitation bacon bits

1. Blend chopped filberts and remaining ingredients, except bread and bacon bits.
2. Spread mixture on bread slices. Cut bread diagonally into quarters. Top each quarter with 1/2 tsp of imitation bacon bits. Place on cookie sheet and bake at 350º for 10 minutes. Serve hot.

What's great about this recipe ?			
"Easy-Fix"	✔	"Bone Health"	
"Quick-Fix"	✔	"Heart Health"	
"Easy-Chew"		"Sweetie"	
"Hands-on"	✔	"High Fiber"	

SuperSource: Chromium

Nutrition information per serving: 134 calories, 12 g carbohydrates, 4 g protein, 8 g fat, 2 g saturated fat, 8 mg cholesterol, 147 mg sodium, 2g fiber. Good source of iron, phosphorus, copper, manganese, selenium.

Ham and Swiss Bites

Servings: 2

Ready in five minutes, these easy-to-eat bites make a tasty party tray. Did you know that mustard can stimulate the appetite? And these are just the right size. When appetite is poor, set out just one or two bites at a time; the appearance of a small bit of food seems more "do-able."

NOTE: high in sodium -- may be inadvisable for those with high blood pressure, congestive heart disease, liver or renal disease.

1 ounce ham	Honey Mustard Dipping Sauce:
1 ounce Swiss cheese	1/4 cup mustard
2 slices whole wheat bread	2 tablespoons honey
1 tablespoon mayonnaise	
toothpicks	

1. Spread bread with mayonnaise. Lay ham and cheese slices on one slice, and top with the second slice. Press down firmly to make the layers stick together. Cut sandwich into bite-sized squares.
2. Combine mustard and honey in a small bowl. Thread two squares onto a toothpick, dunk into sauce.

What's great about this recipe ?

"Easy-Fix"	✔	"Bone Health"	✔
"Quick-Fix"	✔	"Heart Health"	
"Easy-Chew"	✔	"Sweetie"	
"Hands-on"	✔	"High Fiber"	

SuperSource: Phosphorus, manganese, selenium, chromium

Nutrition information per serving: 283 calories, 31 g carbohydrates, 11 g protein, 14 g fat, 4 g saturated fat, 26 mg cholesterol, 800 mg sodium, 2 g fiber. Good source of vitamins B1, B2, B3, B12, K, E, iron, calcium, zinc, copper, manganese, selenium, chromium.

Marinated Shrimp Nibbles

Servings: 4

A versatile and popular recipe. Served on a lettuce leaf or tomato slice, it's a salad. Or, pass out toothpicks, it's a party nibble.* For those who like shrimp, it may tempt the appetite when nothing else does. If you purchase shelled deveined cooked shrimp, it's easy and fast to fix. Although shrimp are high in cholesterol, they're low in fat, especially saturated fat.

1 1/2 teaspoons safflower oil

1 tablespoon fresh ginger root, minced, or 1 tsp dried powdered ginger

1 lime, juiced, or 2 tablespoons bottled lime juice

1 clove garlic, pressed or minced

1/2 tablespoon soy sauce

1/4 teaspoon honey

1/4 teaspoon powdered cayenne or crushed red pepper flakes

1 pound large shrimp, shelled, deveined, tails on, boiled

1/4 cup fresh cilantro, minced

1 large tomato, cut in four thick slices

1. Combine oil, ginger, lime juice, garlic, soy sauce, honey, and red pepper. Stir in cooked shrimp and cilantro. Cover and refrigerate 1 to 4 hours before serving. Stir occasionally while chilling.
2. Put one tomato slice on each of four plates. Divide shrimp equally and pile on tomato slices to serve. Or, place shrimp in bowl, provide cocktail picks so guests can spear and eat as snacks.

What's great about this recipe ?

"Easy-Fix"	✔	"Bone Health"	
"Quick-Fix"		"Heart Health"	
"Easy-Chew"		"Sweetie"	
"Hands-on"	✔*	"High Fiber"	

SuperSource: Iron, B12

Nutrition information per serving: 118 calories, 3 g carbohydrates, 19 g protein, 3 g fat, 0.5 g saturated fat, 173 mg cholesterol, 331 mg sodium, 0 g fiber. Good source of vitamins A, B3, C, phosphorus, zinc, copper, chromium.

Salmon-spinach Party Dip

Servings: 16   Yield: 4 cups

Salmon is a wonderful food, with important omega-3 fatty acids, protein, and B12; while spinach is rich in antioxidants. You can use any crackers or vegetables for dipping or spreading, however, choosing whole grain crackers gives extra fiber. If chewing is a concern, it may be spread on bread instead of crackers or carrots.* Reprinted courtesy of the Alaska Seafood Marketing Institute.

1 (7 1/2-ounce) can salmon
10 ounces frozen chopped spinach, thawed, minced, well drained, and finely chopped
1 cup plain nonfat yogurt
1/2 cup light mayonnaise
1/2 cup parsley, chopped
1/2 cup green onions, chopped

1/2 teaspoon dried basil
1/2 teaspoon dill weed
1/4 teaspoon grated lemon peel
4 carrots, sliced diagonally into ovals, for dipping
16 whole rye crispbread crackers, spread with dip

1. Drain and flake salmon. Combine flaked salmon with remaining ingredients, except raw vegetables and crackers. Chill several hours to blend flavors.
2. Serve dip with vegetables and crackers.

What's great about this recipe ?

"Easy-Fix"	✔	"Bone Health"	✔
"Quick-Fix"		"Heart Health"	✔
"Easy-Chew"	✔*	"Sweetie"	
"Hands-on"	✔	"High Fiber"	✔

SuperSource: Vitamin A, B12

Nutrition information per serving: 103 calories, 13 g carbohydrates, 5 g protein, 4 g fat, 1 g saturated fat, 10 mg cholesterol, 192 mg sodium, 3 g fiber. Good source of vitamins D, K, biotin, iron, phosphorus, manganese, selenium, chromium.

Tuna Tapenade
Servings: 2

This recipe is high in fat, but it's the heart-protective kind of fat – monounsaturated, and omega-3. A good snack for those who need to gain weight. It's quick and easy to make in a blender or food processor. Spread on bread, it's also easy to chew.*

1/4 cup sunflower oil
1/4 cup capers, or less
1 (6.5 ounce) can tuna in oil, drained
1/4 cup lemon juice
2 cloves garlic , minced

1/2 cup pitted black olives
1/8 teaspoon freshly ground pepper
2 carrots, sliced diagonally into ovals
1 cup cauliflower florets
4 whole rye crispbread crackers

1. Place all ingredients except olive oil in a food processor and blend until smooth. Slowly add olive oil. Spread on fresh vegetables or crackers.

What's great about this recipe ?

"Easy-Fix"	✔	"Bone Health"	
"Quick-Fix"	✔	"Heart Health"	✔
"Easy-Chew"	✔*	"Sweetie"	
"Hands-on"	✔	"High Fiber"	

SuperSource: Phosphorus, vitamins A, B3, B12, E

Nutrition information per serving: 307 calories, 14 g carbohydrates, 15 g protein, 21 g fat, 2 g saturated fat, 8 mg cholesterol, 735 mg sodium, 3 g fiber. Good source of vitamins B6, C, iron, manganese, fiber.

"No-Fork Salad"

Servings: 2

This "salad" has everything but the lettuce. All the vegetables are prepared so that they can be easily picked up and dipped. Good for parties, lunch, dinner, or snacks. Vary the dressing ingredients as much as you like – try different vinegars, herbs, or cheeses.

1 medium carrot, sliced diagonally into 1/8" thick oval slices
1 cup cauliflower florets
2 each radishes, trimmed, cut in half
1/2 medium cucumber, sliced diagonally into 1/4" oval slices
1/2 medium red or green bell pepper, sliced in 1/2" wide strips

3 tablespoons sunflower oil
2 tablespoons red wine vinegar
2 teaspoons grated Parmesan cheese
1/4 teaspoon dried basil
1/4 teaspoon dried oregano
1/4 teaspoon dried parsley
1/4 teaspoon salt
1/4 teaspoon freshly ground black pepper

1. Clean and trim the vegetables, slicing as directed.
2. In small bowl whisk together oil, vinegar, cheese, basil, oregano, parsley, salt, and pepper to make a vinaigrette dressing.
3. Arrange the vegetables around the edge of a large plate, with the bowl of dressing in the center. Dip vegetables into dressing.

What's great about this recipe ?

"Easy-Fix"	✔	"Bone Health"	✔
"Quick-Fix"	✔	"Heart Health"	✔
"Easy-Chew"		"Sweetie"	
"Hands-on"	✔	"High Fiber"	

SuperSource: Vitamins A, C, E

Nutrition information per serving: 237 calories, 11 g carbohydrates, 3 g protein, 21 g fat, 3 g saturated fat, 0 mg cholesterol, 359 mg sodium, 4 g fiber. Good source of vitamins B6, E, K, folate, pantothenic acid, potassium, iron, phosphorus, manganese, chromium, fiber.

Hummus

Servings: 3   Yield: 2 cups

This Middle Eastern dish not only tastes delicious, it's a fiber bonanza. NOTE: high in sodium -- may be inadvisable for those with high blood pressure, congestive heart disease, liver or renal disease. To lower the sodium, you can cook the beans yourself, controlling the salt; and you can use fresh vegetables for dippers instead of the higher-sodium pita bread.*

1 (15.5 ounce) can garbanzo beans (chickpeas), drained, reserving liquid
2 medium garlic cloves, or to taste
1/4 cup lemon juice, fresh or bottled
1/4 cup tahini (sesame seed paste)
3 each whole-wheat pita bread rounds, cut in wedges, lightly toasted

1. Place beans and garlic in food processor or blender; process till finely ground.
2. Add lemon juice and tahini, and process till well blended, scraping sides of workbowl.
3. Add reserved liquid, two tablespoons at a time, continuing to process, until desired dipping consistency is achieved.
4. Lightly toast pita wedges. Serve hummus in a bowl with toasted pita wedges for dipping. Makes about 2 cups. Serving size: 2/3 cup hummus, 1 pita loaf.

What's great about this recipe ?			
"Easy-Fix"	✔	"Bone Health"	✔
"Quick-Fix"	✔	"Heart Health"	✔*
"Easy-Chew"		"Sweetie"	
"Hands-on"	✔	"High Fiber"	✔

SuperSource: Iron, phosphorus, copper, manganese, fiber

Nutrition information per serving: 374 calories, 65 g carbohydrates, 15 g protein, 9 g fat, 1 g saturated fat, 0 mg cholesterol, 980 mg sodium, 12 g fiber. Good source of vitamins B1, B3, B6, C, potassium, magnesium, zinc.

Curried Filberts

Servings: 4

A crunchy, tasty snack. You can substitute onion powder for curry or garlic powder, or leave it out entirely. There is some loss of vitamin E with heating, but it's still a nutritious treat. Reprinted courtesy of Dundee Hazelnuts & The Oregon Hazelnut Industry.

1/2 cup hazelnuts (filberts)
1/2 tablespoon olive oil

1/8 teaspoon curry powder or garlic powder
1/8 teaspoon salt

1. Preheat oven to 275 degrees F.
2. In small bowl, stir together nuts, oil, curry powder, and salt. Turn into shallow baking pan.
3. Bake for 20 minutes. Serving size: 2 tablespoons.

What's great about this recipe ?

"Easy-Fix"	✔	"Bone Health"	
"Quick-Fix"	✔	"Heart Health"	
"Easy-Chew"		"Sweetie"	
"Hands-on"	✔	"High Fiber"	

SuperSource: Copper

Nutrition information per serving: 134 calories, 4 g carbohydrates, 3 g protein, 13 g fat, 1 g saturated fat, 0 mg cholesterol, 142 mg sodium, 2 g fiber. Good source of magnesium, manganese.

Glazed Walnuts

Servings: 8   Yield: 1 1/4 cups

Less vitamin E than raw walnuts, but still heart-healthful and a delicious snack for those with a sweet tooth.

1 tablespoon butter or margarine
1 cup English walnut halves (about 8 ounces)

1/4 teaspoon salt
2 tablespoons sugar

1. Melt butter in skillet over medium heat. Add walnut halves. Stir gently til lightly toasted and fragrant, about 3-4 minutes.
2. Add salt and sugar and stir for another 8 to 10 minutes longer, or until sugar caramelizes over walnuts. Do not let them scorch! Spread out on a plate to cool. Serving size: 2 tablespoons.

What's great about this recipe ?

"Easy-Fix"	✔	"Bone Health"	
"Quick-Fix"	✔	"Heart Health"	✔
"Easy-Chew"		"Sweetie"	✔
"Hands-on"	✔	"High Fiber"	

Nutrition information per serving: 122 calories, 6 g carbohydrates, 2 g protein, 11 g fat, 2 g saturated fat, 4 mg cholesterol, 90 mg sodium, 1 g fiber. Good source of copper, manganese, biotin.

Herbed Pecan-Walnut Toss

Servings: 8

Both pecans and walnuts are delicious in their different ways; and both have heart-protective fats, as well as important trace minerals. These make nice nibbles.

1 tablespoon olive oil
1/2 cup pecan halves
1/2 cup English walnut halves
1/4 teaspoon salt

1/4 teaspoon pepper
1/2 teaspoon dried Italian seasoning
   (parsley, basil, oregano)
1/4 teaspoon cayenne

1. In large heavy skillet, warm olive oil over medium heat. Add nuts to hot skillet with salt, pepper, herbs, and cayenne. Stir constantly until nuts are lightly toasted. Remove from heat. Serve warm or cool. Serving size: 2 tablespoons.

What's great about this recipe ?

"Easy-Fix"	✔	"Bone Health"	
"Quick-Fix"	✔	"Heart Health"	✔
"Easy-Chew"		"Sweetie"	
"Hands-on"	✔	"High Fiber"	

Nutrition information per serving: 108 calories, 3 g carbohydrates, 2 g protein, 11 g fat, 1 g saturated fat, 0 mg cholesterol, 73 mg sodium, 1 g fiber. Good source of copper, manganese.

Spicy Fruit and Nuts

Servings: 12   Yield: 1 1/2 cups

Nuts are rich in heart-protective fats, and cherries have many antioxidants. Some loss of vitamin E with cooking. Reprinted courtesy of Cherry Marketing Institute.

1/2 cup English walnut halves
1/2 cup pecan halves
1/2 cup dried tart cherries
1 tablespoon Worcestershire sauce
1/4 teaspoon cayenne pepper, or
   to taste

1/4 teaspoon garlic powder
1/4 teaspoon salt
1/4 teaspoon ground cumin
1/16 teaspoon dried oregano
1 tablespoon olive oil

1. In a medium bowl, combine nuts and cherries. In a small bowl, combine Worcestershire sauce, cayenne, garlic powder, salt, cumin and oregano; mix well. Pour over pecan mixture; stir to coat.
2. Heat oil in a large skillet over medium heat. Add pecan mixture. Cook, stirring constantly, about 5 minutes. Do not allow mixture to burn. Remove from heat. Spread pecans on waxed paper to cool. Store in a tightly covered container. Serving size: 2 tablespoons.

What's great about this recipe ?

"Easy-Fix"	✔	"Bone Health"	
"Quick-Fix"	✔	"Heart Health"	✔
"Easy-Chew"		"Sweetie"	
"Hands-on"	✔	"High Fiber"	

Nutrition information per serving: 85 calories, 5 g carbohydrates, 1 g protein, 7 g fat, 1 g saturated fat, 0 mg cholesterol, 64 mg sodium, 1g fiber. Good source of copper, manganese.

SMOOTHIES, SHAKES AND BEVERAGES

Liquids – our most important nutrient. The adult human body is about 50 to 65 percent water. The human brain is about *75 percent water*. Water is the most important nutrient of all, yet it's the one we're most likely to overlook.

Shakes and smoothies supply water, and are also quick to make and can be just about anything you like: breakfast, lunch, dessert – a meal – a snack. You control the ingredients – high-fiber, high-calcium, thick and creamy, thin, icy, whatever you like.

> Tip: to make a fortified shake or smoothie, add a multivitamin or calcium pill to the blender; grind up and blend right into the drink. You'll have a fortified drink, with no large pill to swallow!

Other beverages can be both refreshing and good for you, too. Green tea, iced tea, even lemonade all have benefits, including increasing our water intake.

> NOTE: Some people find that milk protein blocks the absorption of levodopa to a greater extent, and longer, than other proteins. If you use a medication that contains levodopa, be sure to take it at least 30 minutes before protein-containing drinks; you may find you need to use a milk substitute, such as "soy milk" or Rice Dream, for the cow's milk or yogurt in some of these recipes.

Banana Yogurt Shake

Servings: 2   Yield: 4 Cups

Bananas are a good source of both magnesium and potassium. Yogurt helps maintain the "friendly bacteria" in the colon. Honey contains trace minerals and antioxidants. Reprinted courtesy of The National Honey Board.

2 teaspoons flax seed
1 cup skim milk
1/2 ripe banana, peeled
1/2 cup low-fat plain yogurt
1 tablespoon honey

1/4 teaspoon vanilla
1/8 teaspoon ground cinnamon
Dash ground nutmeg
2 ice cubes

1. Spoon flax seed into blender and grind. Add remaining ingredients except ice cubes and blend until thick and creamy. With motor running, add ice cubes; process until smooth.
2. Pour into tall glasses to serve.

What's great about this recipe ?			
"Easy-Fix"	✔	"Bone Health"	✔
"Quick-Fix"	✔	"Heart Health"	✔
"Easy-Chew"	✔	"Sweetie"	✔
"Hands-on"	✔	"High Fiber"	✔

SuperSource: Vits. B2, B12, phosphorus, manganese, fiber

Nutrition information per serving: 191 calories, 31 g carbohydrates, 9 g protein, 4 g fat, 1 g saturated fat, 6 mg cholesterol, 108 mg sodium, 3 g fiber. Good source of vitamins D, B6, pantothenic acid, biotin, potassium, iron, calcium, magnesium, zinc, copper, selenium.

Banana-Pear Yogurt Smoothie

Servings: 2   Yield: 4 Cups

A sweet and nourishing snack. Did you know that pears are a high-fiber food? Reprinted courtesy of the National Honey Board.

1 teaspoon flax seed
1 16-ounce can pears in juice
1/2 cup low-fat vanilla yogurt
1/2 banana, peeled

3 ice cubes
1 tablespoon honey
Dash ground nutmeg

1. Put flax seed in electric blender and grind.
2. Add pears and their juice, yogurt, banana, ice and honey to blender; blend until smooth.
3. Pour shake into chilled glasses. Sprinkle with nutmeg and serve immediately.

What's great about this recipe ?

"Easy-Fix"	✔	"Bone Health"	
"Quick-Fix"	✔	"Heart Health"	✔
"Easy-Chew"	✔	"Sweetie"	✔
"Hands-on"	✔	"High Fiber"	✔

Nutrition information per serving: 233 calories, 54 g carbohydrates, 4 g protein, 2 g fat, 1 g saturated fat, 4 mg cholesterol, 51 mg sodium, 5 g fiber. Good source of vitamin B6, potassium, iron, copper, manganese, fiber.

Berry Berry Frosty

Servings: 4

Berries have a wealth of valuable anthocyanins, vitamins, minerals, and fiber. This is a delicious drink or dessert, appreciated even more by those who cannot chew well. It's also a good snack choice between meals – being low in protein, it won't block levodopa absorption. Reprinted courtesy of the Oregon Raspberry & Blackberry Commission.

1/2 cup raspberries, fresh or frozen
1/2 cup blackberries, fresh or frozen
1 1/2 cups frozen lowfat yogurt
1 tablespoons sugar
2 tablespoons lemon juice, preferably fresh

Ginger ale or lemon-lime soda
Whole berries for garnish (optional)
Thinly sliced lemon wheels, for garnish (optional)

1. Combine first five ingredients in blender and process until smooth. (If frozen berries are used, partially thaw before blending.)
2. Pour into 4 glasses and slowly add soda to fill each glass.
3. Garnish with 2-3 berries and lemon wheel, if desired.

What's great about this recipe ?

"Easy-Fix"	✔	"Bone Health"	
"Quick-Fix"	✔	"Heart Health"	
"Easy-Chew"	✔	"Sweetie"	✔
"Hands-on"	✔	"High Fiber"	

Nutrition information per serving: 136 calories, 26 g carbohydrates, 2 g protein, 3 g fat, 2 g saturated fat, 1 mg cholesterol, 52 mg sodium, 2 g fiber. Good source of vitamin B2, C, phosphorus, manganese.

Blueberry Fruit Shake

Servings: 3   Yield: 2 1/2 cups

Want to get the recommended 2-3 servings of fruit daily? This is fast, easy, and delicious. It's also a good snack choice between meals – it's low in protein, and won't block levodopa absorption. Reprinted courtesy of the North American Blueberry Council.

2 cups frozen blueberries
1 cup frozen mixed fruit (cantaloupe, honeydew, grapes, peaches, etc.)

1 cup skim milk
1 tablespoon sugar
2 teaspoons vanilla extract

1. In the container of a food processor or blender, place blueberries, mixed fruit, milk, sugar and vanilla extract; whirl until smooth. Serve immediately.

What's great about this recipe ?

"Easy-Fix"	✔	"Bone Health"	
"Quick-Fix"	✔	"Heart Health"	✔
"Easy-Chew"	✔	"Sweetie"	✔
"Hands-on"	✔	"High Fiber"	✔

SuperSource: Vitamin C

Nutrition information per serving: 131 calories, 29 g carbohydrates, 4 g protein, 1 g fat, 0 g saturated fat, 1 mg cholesterol, 50 mg sodium, 3 g fiber. Good source of vitamin A, B2, B12, potassium, phosphorus, copper, manganese, fiber.

Orangey Banana Breakfast Shake

Servings: 1   Yield: 2 Cups

Here's a recipe that's got it all – minerals, vitamins, fiber, and it tastes great!! Your bones and heart will especially thank you every time you make this shake. If you use levodopa, and are sensitive to the protein in cow's milk, try calcium-fortified soy milk or Rice Dream instead.

1 teaspoon flax seed
1/4 cup calcium-fortified orange juice
   concentrate

1 cup low-fat or skim milk
2 teaspoons honey or sugar
1 ripe banana

1. Place flax seed in blender, and grind.
2. Add remaining ingredients and blend till smooth.

What's great about this recipe ?

"Easy-Fix"	✔	"Bone Health"	✔
"Quick-Fix"	✔	"Heart Health"	✔
"Easy-Chew"	✔	"Sweetie"	✔
"Hands-on"	✔	"High Fiber"	✔

> **SuperSource:** Vitamins B1, B2, B6, B12, C, D, folate, pantothenic acid, potassium, magnesium, phosphorus, copper, manganese, fiber.

Nutrition information per serving: 454 calories, 91 g carbohydrates, 13 g protein, 5 g fat, 2 g saturated fat, 10 mg cholesterol, 130 mg sodium, 7 g fiber. Good source of vitamins A, B3, biotin, K, iron, calcium, zinc.

Strawberry-Banana Smoothie

Servings: 2   Yield: 3/4 cup

If you'd like to gain weight, add a teaspoon or two of sunflower seed oil – it will add calories, and is rich in vitamin E as well. Reprinted courtesy of Sue Bee Honey.

1 teaspoon flax seed   1/2 cup skim or 1% milk
1 cup frozen strawberries   1 tablespoon honey
1/2 banana   1/2 teaspoon vanilla
1/2 8-ounce container lemon yogurt

1. Add flax seed to electric blender container, and grind.
2. Add remaining ingredients and blend til smooth.

What's great about this recipe ?			
"Easy-Fix"	✔	"Bone Health"	✔
"Quick-Fix"	✔	"Heart Health"	✔
"Easy-Chew"	✔	"Sweetie"	✔
"Hands-on"	✔	"High Fiber"	✔

SuperSource: Vitamin C, fiber

Nutrition information per serving: 174 calories, 35 g carbohydrates, 6 g protein, 2 g fat, 1 g saturated fat, 5 mg cholesterol, 75 mg sodium, 3 g fiber. Good source of vitamins B2, B6, biotin, K, potassium, iron, calcium, phosphorus, copper, manganese.

Eastern Fruit Smoothie

Servings: 4   Yield: 5 Cups

There are lots of good things to say about soy – it gives a wonderful, smooth texture to shakes, it's a complete protein, and for many people, soy protein does not interfere with levodopa absorption to the same extent that milk does. For extra calcium, add a calcium tablet to the blender, grind well, then add the remaining ingredients. Reprinted courtesy of the Indiana Soybean Board.

1 (10.5-ounce) package soft lite silken tofu
1 medium banana
1 8-ounce can unsweetened crushed pineapple, chilled

2 cups unsweetened orange-pineapple juice, chilled (you can also use plain orange juice, calcium-fortified if you need extra calcium)

1. Combine all ingredients in electric blender; cover and process until smooth. Serve immediately.

What's great about this recipe ?

"Easy-Fix"	✔	"Bone Health"	
"Quick-Fix"	✔	"Heart Health"	✔
"Easy-Chew"	✔	"Sweetie"	✔
"Hands-on"	✔	"High Fiber"	✔

SuperSource: Vitamin C, manganese, fiber

Nutrition information per serving: 155 calories, 30 g carbohydrates, 7 g protein, 1 g fat, 0 g saturated fat, 0 mg cholesterol, 67 mg sodium, 3 g fiber. Good source of vitamin B1, B6, potassium, iron, phosphorus, copper.

Hot Ginger Tea *

Yield: 2 cups

For many people, ginger can relieve the nausea that Parkinson medications often cause. Here's a recipe to try. Look for a good-quality brand of ginger tea in the herbal tea section of your supermarket or health food store.

2 tea bags of ginger tea   2 cups boiling water
dash ground cinnamon (optional)   honey to taste
dash ground cloves (optional)

1. Place tea bags, cinnamon, and cloves in a teapot. Pour boiling water over. Steep 3-5 minutes. Serve with a teaspoon of honey or to taste.

Fresh Ginger Tea *

Some people find that fresh ginger is superior to dried, powdered ginger in relieving nausea. Here's another recipe to try. Fresh ginger root is available in many supermarkets.

1 tablespoon grated fresh ginger
16 ounces water

1. Place ginger and water in a small saucepan, tightly covered, and bring to a simmer; simmer, covered, about 5 minutes. Turn off heat and let the tea steep, covered, an additional 15 minutes.
2. Sip slowly, or take an ounce every 30 minutes. You may add lemon and honey if you like.

---

* NOTE: Ginger may have blood-thinning properties. Persons using blood-thinning medications such as Coumadin (warfarin), heparin, Plavix (clopidogrel), Ticlid (ticlopidine), Trental (pentoxifylline), or aspirin should ask their doctors before using ginger. Large overdoses can cause CNS depression and cardiac arrhythmia; use with moderation. Also, safety in pregnant or nursing women, young children, or individuals with severe liver or kidney disease has not been established.

Black and Green Teas

There's good news about tea – black tea, green tea, even, to a lesser extent, decaffeinated and instant versions of these teas.

Black tea contains *flavonoids* – compounds also known as phytochemicals – that act as antioxidants and counteract the damaging effects of free radicals. Free radical damage can lead to heart disease and cancers, so protective antioxidants are a powerful tool in fighting disease. The compounds of importance in black tea are called thearubigins and theaflavins and appear to be protective against heart attacks. Theaflavin is being studied for a possible protective effect against colon cancer.

Green tea also contains flavonoids, though different ones, called catechins. It, too, may protect against some cancers, including stomach and breast cancers. Still better, green tea contains polyphenols, another antioxidant that is being studied to see if it might protect against the damage to neurons that occurs in Parkinson's disease.

Black, green, and oolong teas all appear to help maintain bone density, protecting against osteoporosis and fractures. This may be due to the fluoride contained in tea; fluoride is important in helping maintain bone strength.

But whether or not tea is protective, it tastes good, the caffeine is a "pick-me-up," and it helps boost fluid intake and protect against urinary tract infections. If you prefer the taste of black tea, but want the benefits of green tea, just use a teabag of each.

To release the flavonoids, let tea steep at least five minutes. You can drink it hot or iced, or mix it with fruit juices if you prefer, you'll still get all the benefits of the tea. The following pages contain some recipes you might like to try.

Decaffeinated teas and instant teas lose some, though not all, of the protective phytochemicals. But if you cannot tolerate caffeine, it's worthwhile drinking the decaf version. Herbal teas do not contain the same protective phytochemicals as black and green teas.

> NOTE: Don't drink too much tea. Black and green teas contain tannins, which bind with dietary iron and prevent its absorption. Tea may also interfere with warfarin (coumadin), a blood-thinning medication. Persons using warfarin should discuss use of tea with their physicians.

Green Tea Sipper

Servings: 2

Some people don't like the taste of plain green tea, so here's a way to provide both flavor and extra nutrition.

2 bags green tea
1 1/2 cups boiling water
1 cup calcium-fortified orange juice

1 tablespoon lemon juice
1 teaspoon honey (or to taste)

1. Place tea bags in teapot or small saucepan; pour boiling water over, and cover. Let steep 10-15 minutes. Place in refrigerator to cool.
2. Add orange juice, lemon juice and honey to taste.
3. Pour into tall glasses with ice.

What's great about this recipe ?

"Easy-Fix"	✔	"Bone Health"	
"Quick-Fix"		"Heart Health"	✔
"Easy-Chew"	✔	"Sweetie"	✔
"Hands-on"	✔	"High Fiber"	

SuperSource: Vitamin C

Nutrition information per serving: 69 calories, 17 g carbohydrates, 0 g protein, 0 g fat, 0 g saturated fat, 0 mg cholesterol, 7 mg sodium, 0 g fiber. Good source of folate, calcium, manganese.

Green Tea Ginger Sparkler *

Servings: 4   Yield: 4 1/4 cups

Here's a zingy drink for a hot summer day. And, good news, ginger can help some folks combat the nausea caused by PD medications.* Reprinted courtesy of Stash Tea.

1 1/3 cups tea concentrate (made from Stash Tea Premium Green tea)**

1/4 cup finely chopped crystallized ginger
2 2/3 cups chilled ginger ale
Ice cubes

1. Combine ginger and tea concentrate while still hot and refrigerate for at least three hours. Strain and discard ginger. Pour concentrate and ginger ale into ice filled glasses.

---

* NOTE: Ginger may have blood-thinning properties. Persons using blood-thinning medications such as Coumadin (warfarin), heparin, Plavix (clopidogrel), Ticlid (ticlopidine), Trental (pentoxifylline), or aspirin should ask their doctors before using ginger. Large overdoses can cause CNS depression and cardiac arrhythmia; use with moderation. Also, safety in pregnant or nursing women, young children, or individuals with severe liver or kidney disease has not been established.

** Steep 12 green tea bags in 4 cups boiling water for 10 minutes. Squeeze bags to press out all the liquid. Cool concentrate in the refrigerator at least 3 hours and up to 2 weeks.

What's great about this recipe ?

"Easy-Fix"	✔	"Bone Health"	
"Quick-Fix"		"Heart Health"	
"Easy-Chew"	✔	"Sweetie"	✔
"Hands-on"	✔	"High Fiber"	

Nutrition information per serving: 59 calories, 15 g carbohydrates, 0 g protein, 0 g fat, 0 g saturated fat, 0 mg cholesterol, 11 mg sodium, 0 g fiber. Good source of iron.

Cran-Tea Cooler

Serving: 1

If you love iced tea, and you also love the tang of cranberry juice, you can have the best of both – just stir them together! Also, cranberry juice may help protect against urinary tract infections, which can be a problem for some folks with PD.

1 bag black tea
6 ounces boiling water

4 ounces cranberry juice cocktail

1. Place tea bag in teapot or small saucepan. Pour boiling water over tea bag and cover. Let steep 5 minutes. Remove tea bag and put tea in refrigerator to cool.
2. Add cranberry juice cocktail to cold tea and pour into a tall glass over ice.

What's great about this recipe ?

"Easy-Fix"	✔	"Bone Health"	
"Quick-Fix"	✔	"Heart Health"	
"Easy-Chew"	✔	"Sweetie"	
"Hands-on"	✔	"High Fiber"	

SuperSource: Vitamin C, manganese

Nutrition information per serving: 74 calories, 19 g carbohydrates, 0 g protein, 0 g fat, 0 g saturated fat, 0 mg cholesterol, 8 mg sodium, 0 g fiber.

BREAKFAST

Breakfast doesn't have to be cereal with milk, or steak and eggs – although it can be. And you don't have to eat it the second you get out of bed. Breakfast can be anything you like, eaten when you get hungry. The important thing is to start getting the vitamins, minerals, fiber, and other nutrients you need. If you use a medication that contains levodopa, however, you'll need to take this at least 30 minutes before eating breakfast.

A fruit smoothie is an excellent breakfast, and you can vary it according to whatever fruits are available. On the other hand, what's better than a hot muffin in the morning? Or eggs with whole-wheat toast and jam? Well, maybe pancakes or French toast! You'll find a variety of different breakfast ideas here – and you don't have to eat them at breakfast. If you'd like a muffin for dinner, or French toast at lunch – or soup for breakfast – that's fine.

Are eggs OK? It's true that eggs are high in cholesterol – but most experts now agree that a few eggs a week are fine. Eggs are a rich source of many vital nutrients, as well as exceptionally high-quality protein. So, unless your doctor or dietitian has advised otherwise, serve eggs with your favorite fruit juice, toast or potatoes, for a hard-to-beat start to the day.

Easy Speedy Fruit-Filled Omelet

Servings: 1

A new way to increase those important fruit servings. Reprinted courtesy of the California Egg Commission.

2 large eggs
2 tablespoons water
1 teaspoon butter or margarine

1/2 cup fresh or frozen blackberries, raspberries, or blueberries
1 teaspoon powdered sugar

1. Beat together 2 eggs and 2 tablespoons of water.
2. In 7-10" omelet pan or skillet, over medium heat, heat 1 teaspoon butter or margarine until just hot enough to sizzle a drop of water. Pour in egg mixture. Mixture should set immediately at edges.
3. With an inverted pancake turner, carefully push cooked portions at edges toward center so uncooked portions can reach hot pan surface.
4. While drawing cooked portions toward center, tilt pan and move cooked portions as necessary.
5. While top is still moist and creamy-looking, spoon berries on one side of omelet. With pancake turner, fold unfilled side of omelet over filling. Don't worry if it tears. When flipped onto plate, tears won't be visible.
6. Slide omelet from pan onto plate or invert onto plate with a quick flip of the wrist. Dust with powdered sugar.

What's great about this recipe ?			
"Easy-Fix"	✔	"Bone Health"	✔
"Quick-Fix"	✔	"Heart Health"	
"Easy-Chew"	✔	"Sweetie"	✔
"Hands-on"		"High Fiber"	✔

SuperSource: Vitamins A, B2, B12, K, pantothenic acid, biotin, phosphorus, manganese, selenium, fiber

Nutrition information per serving: 231 calories, 13 g carbohydrates, 13 g protein, 14 g fat, 6 g saturated fat, 435 mg cholesterol, 321 mg sodium, 4 g fiber. Good source of vitamins C, D, E, folate, iron, zinc, copper, chromium.

Crustless Quiche

Servings: 1

For those with a small appetite, the quiche can be cut in half; half can be refrigerated, then warmed and eaten an hour or so later. Serve with a glass of fruit juice and a slice of whole-grain toast, if you wish. This recipe can easily be doubled for two servings.

Cooking spray
3 tablespoons shredded Cheddar cheese, lightly packed
1/4 cup canned low-sodium asparagus
2 tablespoons chopped red onion or sweet onion

2 tablespoons sliced mushrooms (fresh or canned)
2 eggs
1/4 cup 1% milk
Pepper, to taste

1. Preheat oven to 375° degrees. Spray a one-quart round baking dish (about 6" across the bottom) with cooking spray. Spread cheese on bottom of pan and scatter asparagus, onion, and mushrooms over cheese.
2. Whisk together eggs, milk, and pepper. Pour over cheese and vegetables. Bake about 25-35 minutes or until knife inserted in center comes out clean.

What's great about this recipe ?

"Easy-Fix"	✔	"Bone Health"	✔
"Quick-Fix"		"Heart Health"	
"Easy-Chew"	✔	"Sweetie"	
"Hands-on"		"High Fiber"	

SuperSource: Vitamins A, B2, folate, B12, pantothenic acid, biotin, K, iron, phosphorus, selenium, chromium

Nutrition information per serving: 281 calories, 8 g carbohydrates, 21 g protein, 18 g fat, 8 g saturated fat, 449 mg cholesterol, 460 mg sodium, 1 g fiber. Good source of vitamins B1, B6, C, D, potassium, calcium, zinc, copper.

Breakfast Egg-Spinach Bake

Servings: 2

Sometimes folks who don't like spinach find it acceptable when cooked into other dishes. If so, this is a delicious way to include a dark green leafy vegetable. If you are on a low-cholesterol diet, you may substitute two egg whites for each whole egg, or use a yolk-free egg product.

Cooking spray
4 large eggs
1 cup frozen chopped spinach, thawed
1/4 teaspoon pepper
1 teaspoon mustard (optional)

1/4 cup 1% milk
1 slice whole wheat bread, cut in 1/2" cubes
1 ounce Swiss cheese, grated (1/4 cup)
1/2 cup chopped tomato

1. Preheat oven to 375 degrees.
2. Spray 8" casserole dish with nonstick cooking spray.
3. In medium bowl, lightly beat eggs with fork. Add thawed spinach, and stir to mix. Add pepper to taste, mustard, and milk. Stir to mix well. Stir in bread cubes.
4. Pour into casserole dish, top with grated Swiss cheese. Bake for 30 minutes or until set.
5. Serve with chopped tomatoes as garnish.

What's great about this recipe ?

"Easy-Fix"	✔	"Bone Health"	✔
"Quick-Fix"		"Heart Health"	
"Easy-Chew"	✔	"Sweetie"	
"Hands-on"		"High Fiber"	

SuperSource: Vitamins A, B2, B12, K, folate, pantothenic acid, biotin, iron, calcium, phosphorus, manganese, selenium, chromium

Nutrition information per serving: 282 calories, 16 g carbohydrates, 22 g protein, 15 g fat, 6 g saturated fat, 438 mg cholesterol, 365 mg sodium, 4 g fiber. Good source of vitamins B1, B6, C, D, E, potassium, magnesium, zinc, copper, fiber.

Broccoli Breakfast Casseroles

Servings: 4

This is a tasty way to get a serving of vegetables for breakfast! Add a serving of fresh fruit or a glass of fruit juice for balance. If you purchase ready-grated cheese, it's really quick to prepare.

Cooking spray
4 slices whole-wheat bread
1 cup frozen chopped broccoli, thawed
2 cups grated Cheddar or Swiss cheese
5 large eggs
1 cup skim or 1% milk

1/4 tsp dried oregano
1/4 tsp dried basil
1/4 tsp dried parsley
1/2 teaspoon pepper
1 green onion, thinly sliced (or 1 1/2 teaspoons dehydrated onion)
2 slices whole wheat bread, cubed

1. Preheat oven to 350 degrees F.
2. Spray 4 individual 4-6"casserole dishes with cooking spray. Press a slice of whole-wheat bread firmly in the bottom of each dish. Divide the broccoli and cheese among the dishes.
3. In a medium bowl beat together with a wire whisk the eggs, milk, oregano, basil, parsley, pepper and green onion. Divide among the casserole dishes. Top each dish with some bread cubes.
4. Place casseroles on a baking sheet and bake 20 minutes or until eggs are set and the bread cubes are golden brown.

What's great about this recipe ?			
"Easy-Fix"	✔	"Bone Health"	✔
"Quick-Fix"	✔	"Heart Health"	
"Easy-Chew"	✔	"Sweetie"	
"Hands-on"		"High Fiber"	

SuperSource: Vitamins A, B2, B12, C, K, pantothenic acid, biotin, iron, phosphorus, manganese, selenium, chromium

Nutrition information per serving: 328 calories, 24 g carbohydrates, 21 g protein, 17 g fat, 8 g saturated fat, 296 mg cholesterol, 575 mg sodium, 4 g fiber. Good source of vitamins B1, B3, B6, D, E, folate, potassium, calcium, magnesium, zinc, copper, fiber.

Fruity Potato Breakfast Squares

Servings: 6

Here's a "one-pot" breakfast – fruit, eggs, and potatoes. To make it go faster, microwave the potatoes instead of baking them. Reprinted courtesy of the Idaho Potato Commission.

1/2 teaspoon butter

4 (9 ounce) russet baking potatoes, baked, cooled, and sliced 3/8"

1/2 cup mixed dried fruit (raisins, cranberries, cherries, chopped apricots, etc.)

4 large eggs

1 cup evaporated skim milk

1/2 teaspoon salt

1/4 teaspoon freshly ground pepper

1 cup maple syrup (optional)

1. Butter a 7 × 11 -inch baking pan.
2. Preheat oven to 350 degrees F. Arrange half the sliced potatoes in the buttered pan. Cover potatoes evenly with the dried fruit. Top fruit layer with remaining potato slices.
3. Mix eggs, milk, salt and pepper in a separate bowl and pour over potatoes. Place pan of potatoes in a larger baking pan (such as a 13 × 9-inch pan) and carefully pour 1/2 inch of boiling water into the larger pan to create a water bath. Cover potatoes with foil and bake 40 minutes.
4. Uncover potatoes and bake another 15 minutes or until a knife inserted in the center comes out clean. Remove from oven, cut into 6 squares; serve with maple syrup if desired.

What's great about this recipe ?

"Easy-Fix"	✔	"Bone Health"	✔
"Quick-Fix"		"Heart Health"	✔
"Easy-Chew"	✔	"Sweetie"	
"Hands-on"		"High Fiber"	

SuperSource: Vitamins B2, B6, C, pantothenic acid, potassium, iron, phosphorus, copper

Nutrition information per serving: 434 calories, 90 g carbohydrates, 12 g protein, 4 g fat, 1 g saturated fat, 144 mg cholesterol, 359 mg sodium, 5 g fiber. Good source of vitamins A, B1, B3, B12, K, biotin, calcium, magnesium, zinc, manganese, selenium, fiber.

Potato and Egg Scramble

Servings: 4

Leaving the peel on the potatoes adds fiber and nutrients to this quick-fix dish. Reprinted courtesy of The Idaho Potato Commission.

1 large russet or other baking potato, diced
1/4 cup chopped onion
1/4 cup chopped green or red bell pepper

4 eggs
1/4 cup skim milk
1/4 teaspoon salt
1/8 teaspoon pepper
Dash garlic powder

1. Combine potato, onion and bell pepper in a 9-inch microwave-safe pie plate. Cover with microwavable plastic wrap and microwave at HIGH 4 to 5 minutes, or until potato is tender.
2. Combine eggs, milk, salt, pepper and garlic powder in a medium bowl; beat slightly. Pour over potatoes in pie plate. Cover with microwavable plastic wrap and microwave at HIGH 4 minutes, stirring after 2 minutes.
3. Let stand, covered, 1 minute. Serve immediately.

What's great about this recipe ?

"Easy-Fix"	✔	"Bone Health"	✔
"Quick-Fix"	✔	"Heart Health"	✔
"Easy-Chew"	✔	"Sweetie"	
"Hands-on"		"High Fiber"	

SuperSource: Biotin, chromium

Nutrition information per serving: 157 calories, 19 g carbohydrates, 9 g protein, 5 g fat, 2 g saturated fat, 212 mg cholesterol, 299 mg sodium, 2 g fiber. Good source of vitamins A, B2, B6, B12, C, K, pantothenic acid, potassium, iron, phosphorus, copper, selenium.

Baked Cinnamon-Raisin Oatmeal

Servings: 4

An entirely new way to eat oatmeal. If you use levodopa and find that cow's milk blocks levodopa absorption, you may want to substitute soy milk instead. The apple and pear are optional, but add sweetness and lots of fiber. *To make it "easy-chew" stir them in before baking.* *

Cooking spray
3 cups quick cooking oats
1 teaspoon baking powder
1 teaspoon cinnamon
1/4 cup brown sugar
1/4 cup raisins
2 large eggs

2 cups skim or 1% milk
1 teaspoon vanilla
2 tablespoons butter, melted
1 apple, cored and diced 1/2" (optional)
1 pear, cored and diced 1/2" (optional)

1. Preheat oven to 350 degrees F. Spray 9" x 9" baking dish with cooking spray.
2. In medium bowl, stir together oats, baking powder, cinnamon, and brown sugar, till well combined. Stir in raisins.
3. In small bowl, whisk eggs till foamy. Whisk in milk, then vanilla, then butter. Gradually add dry ingredients, stirring till blended.
4. Spoon into baking dish and bake at 350 for 45 minutes.
5. Divide among four dishes. Top with chopped fruit. Serve with milk if desired.

What's great about this recipe ?

"Easy-Fix"		"Bone Health"	✔
"Quick-Fix"		"Heart Health"	✔
"Easy-Chew"	✔*	"Sweetie"	✔
"Hands-on"		"High Fiber"	✔

SuperSource: Vit.B1, B2, B12, pant.acid, biotin, iron, magnesium, phosphorus, zinc, copper, manganese, chromium, fiber.

Nutrition information per serving: 496 calories, 80 g carbohydrates, 18 g protein, 13 g fat, 5 g saturated fat, 125 mg cholesterol, 304 mg sodium, 9 g fiber. Good source of vitamins A, B6, D, K, potassium, calcium, selenium.

Orange-Blueberry Whole Wheat Griddle Cakes

Servings: 4

A tasty way to get the benefits of blueberries – and this recipe packs an extra punch: the antioxidant-rich orange juice, plus calcium, and fiber, too. If you find that milk blocks levodopa absorption, try this recipe – it's milk-free!

2 cups whole wheat flour, lightly spooned into measuring cup
1/2 teaspoon baking soda
1/2 teaspoon salt
2 eggs

1/4 cup oil (preferably sunflower or safflower oil)
2 cups calcium-fortified orange juice
1 cup fresh or frozen blueberries
1 cup maple syrup

1. In medium bowl, stir flour, baking soda, and salt until well mixed. In separate bowl, whisk eggs till frothy. Whisk in oil, then orange juice until well blended. Add dry ingredients a cup at a time, whisking lightly till mixed. Stir in blueberries.

2. Heat skillet or griddle over medium heat. Flick a drop of water onto the pan; if it sizzles, the pan is hot enough. Ladle batter in 1/4 to 1/2 cup amounts onto pan (depending on how large you like your hot cakes). Bake till golden brown, flip over and bake other side. Serve with maple syrup.

What's great about this recipe ?

"Easy-Fix"	✔	"Bone Health"	✔
"Quick-Fix"	✔	"Heart Health"	✔
"Easy-Chew"	✔	"Sweetie"	✔
"Hands-on"		"High Fiber"	✔

SuperSource: Vits.B1, B3, C, E, K, biotin, iron, phosphorus, copper, manganese, fiber

Nutrition information per serving: 628 calories, 112 g carbohydrates, 12 g protein, 17 g fat, 3 g saturated fat, 106 mg cholesterol, 531 mg sodium, 8 g fiber. Good source of vits. B2, B6, folate, pant. acid, potassium, calcium, magnesium, zinc, selenium.

Banana-Oat Pancakes

Servings: 4   Yield: 12 Pancakes

For those who would like to incorporate more soy into their meals for its health benefits, this is a good way to start out the day. If it's hard to manipulate a fork and knife, try rolling the pancake, and dipping it in the syrup* – you may start a new trend! Reprinted courtesy of the Indiana Soybean Board.

1/2 cup rolled oats	1 1/2 cups plain soymilk
1/2 cup unbleached flour	2 bananas, chopped 1/2"
1/4 cup soy flour	1 cup maple syrup
1 tablespoon baking powder	

1. In a large bowl, combine the rolled oats, unbleached flour, soy flour, and baking powder. Add the soymilk, and blend with a few swift strokes. Fold in the chopped banana.
2. Pour 1/4 cup of the batter onto a hot nonstick griddle or pan. Cook for about 2 minutes or until bubbles appear on the surface. Flip the pancake and cook for another minute or until heated through.
3. Serve the pancakes with maple syrup. Alternatively serve with unsweetened applesauce.

What's great about this recipe ?

"Easy-Fix"	✔	"Bone Health"	✔
"Quick-Fix"	✔	"Heart Health"	✔
"Easy-Chew"	✔	"Sweetie"	✔
"Hands-on"	✔*	"High Fiber"	

SuperSource: Vit. B1, B2, iron, copper, manganese

Nutrition information per serving: 419 calories, 91 g carbohydrates, 9 g protein, 3 g fat, 0 g saturated fat, 0 mg cholesterol, 362 mg sodium, 3 g fiber. Good source of vitamins B3, B6, biotin, potassium, calcium, magnesium, phosphorus, fiber.

Blueberry-stuffed French Toast

Servings: 8

A delicious recipe for special mornings; the recipe can be easily cut in half. Reprinted courtesy of The North American Blueberry Council.

Cooking spray
6 eggs
1 teaspoon grated orange peel (optional)
2/3 cup calcium-fortified orange juice
3 tablespoons sugar, divided

1 cup fresh or frozen blueberries (thawed and drained, if frozen)
8 slices Italian bread, 1-1/4 inches thick
1/3 cup sliced almonds
8 teaspoons butter
1 cup maple syrup

1. Preheat oven to 400ºF. Spray a large baking sheet with cooking spray.
2. In a medium bowl beat eggs, orange peel, juice, and 2 tablespoons of the sugar, until well blended. Pour into a 13 × 9 × 2-inch baking pan; set aside.
3. In a small bowl combine blueberries and the remaining 1 tablespoon sugar; set aside.
4. With the tip of a sharp knife, cut a 1-1/2-inch wide pocket in the side of each bread slice. Fill pockets with reserved blueberry mixture, dividing evenly. Place filled slices in egg mixture. Let stand, turning once, until egg mixture is absorbed, about 5 minutes on each side.
5. Arrange bread on prepared baking sheet. Bake 10 minutes; turn slices and sprinkle with almonds. Bake about 5 minutes longer, until golden brown.
6. Serve with 1 teaspoon butter and 2 tablespoons of maple syrup per slice.

What's great about this recipe ?			
"Easy-Fix"		"Bone Health"	✔
"Quick-Fix"		"Heart Health"	✔
"Easy-Chew"		"Sweetie"	✔
"Hands-on"		"High Fiber"	

SuperSource: Vits. B2, biotin

Nutrition information per serving: 328 calories, 48 g carbohydrates, 8 g protein, 12 g fat, 4 g saturated fat, 170 mg cholesterol, 311 mg sodium, 2 g fiber. Good source of vitamins A, E, B1, B12, K, pant. acid, iron, phosphorus, copper, manganese, selenium, chromium.

Crunchy French Toast

Servings: 2

The crunchy bran flakes add a whole new dimension of enjoyment to French toast. Incidentally, they also add fiber! If it's hard to manipulate eating utensils, cut the browned slices into 1"-wide sticks before serving; they can then be dipped into a shallow bowl of syrup – no need for forks or knives.*

1 large egg
1/3 cup skim or 1% milk
2 teaspoons sugar
1/4 teaspoon cinnamon
1/4 cup flaked coconut

1 1/2 cups bran flakes, coarsely crushed (about 1/2 cup total)
4 slices whole wheat bread
1/2 cup maple syrup

1. In medium mixing bowl, whisk together egg, milk, sugar and cinnamon.
2. On a plate, stir together coconut and crushed bran flakes.
3. Spray skillet with cooking spray. Heat skillet over medium heat.
4. Dip bread slices in egg mixture, then in coconut mixture, on both sides.
5. Brown in skillet until light golden on both sides, turning once. Serve with maple syrup.

What's great about this recipe ?			
"Easy-Fix"	✔	"Bone Health"	✔
"Quick-Fix"	✔	"Heart Health"	✔
"Easy-Chew"	✔	"Sweetie"	✔
"Hands-on"	✔*	"High Fiber"	✔

SuperSource: Vits. A, E, B1, B2, B3, B6, B12, folate, biotin, iron, magnesium, phosphorus, zinc, copper, selenium, chromium, fiber

Nutrition information per serving: 546 calories, 111 g carbohydrates, 14 g protein, 8 g fat, 4 g saturated fat, 107 mg cholesterol, 652 mg sodium, 12 g fiber. Good source of vitamins C, D, K, pant. acid, potassium, calcium, manganese.

Hot Quinoa-Fruit Breakfast Cereal
Servings: 2

Quinoa is one of the few grains that has complete protein. It can be hard to find, but should be available in health food stores. If cow's milk blocks levodopa absorption, try a calcium-fortified soy milk or Rice Dream instead.

1 cup quinoa	1/2 teaspoon cinnamon
2 cups water	1/2 cup skim milk
1/2 cup apple, chopped 1/2"	2 tablespoons honey
1/3 cup raisins	

1. Rinse quinoa thoroughly and add to water; bring to a boil. Reduce heat; simmer for 5 minutes. Add apples, raisins and cinnamon; simmer until water is absorbed.
2. Serve with milk and honey.

What's great about this recipe ?

"Easy-Fix"	✔	"Bone Health"	✔
"Quick-Fix"	✔	"Heart Health"	✔
"Easy-Chew"	✔	"Sweetie"	
"Hands-on"		"High Fiber"	✔

SuperSource: Vits. B2, potassium, iron, magnesium, phosphorus, zinc, copper, manganese, fiber

---

Nutrition information per serving: 498 calories, 104 g carbohydrates, 14 g protein, 5 g fat, 1 g saturated fat, 1 mg cholesterol, 53 mg sodium, 7 g fiber. Good source of vits. B1, B3, B6, folate, pant.acid, chromium.

Great Granola

Servings: 12   Serving size: 3/4 cup
This takes awhile to prepare, but it's worth it, for its wealth of nutrients!

4 cups rolled oats
2 cups rolled wheat
1/2 cup wheat bran
1/2 cup peanut oil
1 teaspoon ground cinnamon
1/2 teaspoon ground cloves
1/4 cup honey or maple syrup
1/2 cup raw wheat germ

1 cup ground flax seed
1 cup raw sunflower seeds
1 cup raw almonds
1/2 cup raw walnuts
1/2 cup dried apricots, chopped
1/2 cup dried cranberries
1 cup raisins

1. In large bowl, mix together rolled oats, rolled wheat, and bran.
2. In small saucepan, on low heat, warm oil, cinnamon, cloves, and honey, til mixture is thin. Pour over oat mixture and stir to combine thoroughly.
3. Spoon into two 9" x 12" x 2" baking pans. (Alternatively, spoon into crockery cooker; cook for 3-4 hours. Add wheat germ, flax, sunflower seeds, almonds, and walnuts, stirring well. Replace lid, turn off cooker, and allow to cool. Stir in fruits.)
4. Preheat oven to 250 degrees F. Bake mixture 2 hours, stirring every 15 minutes, until golden brown. Remove from oven. Add wheat germ, flax, sunflower seeds, almonds, and walnuts; bake for 15 minutes, then remove from oven and allow to cool. Stir in fruits.
5. Store in airtight container. If you intend to keep it for more than a week, store in the freezer.

What's great about this recipe ?			
"Easy-Fix"	✔	"Bone Health"	✔
"Quick-Fix"		"Heart Health"	✔
"Easy-Chew"		"Sweetie"	✔
"Hands-on"		"High Fiber"	✔

SuperSource: Vits. E, B1, B2, B3, B6, B12, folate, pant.acid, iron, magnesium, phosphorus, zinc, copper, manganese, fiber

Nutrition information per serving: 453 calories, 52 g carbohydrates, 12 g protein, 26 g fat, 3 g saturated fat, 0 mg cholesterol, 52 mg sodium, 10 g fiber. Good source of vits. A, C, biotin, potassium, calcium, selenium.

MAIN DISHES

Main dishes should be hearty and satisfying, the *soul* of the meal. Ideally, they should also be rich in protective nutrients, and PD-friendly fiber. I've included some with meat and poultry, however, you'll find an emphasis on fish, nuts, seeds, whole grains and legumes (dried beans). This is because fish oils help combat heart disease, and may help fight depression as well; nuts and seeds contain heart-protective fats and many trace minerals not easily found in other foods; while legumes and whole grains are among the foods highest in fibers, as well as the protective B vitamins, and health-preserving minerals.

It's a good idea to vary your meals throughout the week; that way you'll get the widest variety of nutrients. Spread among the morning, midday, and evening meals, I recommend:

- fish three to four times a week
- legumes and whole grains daily or every other day
- two or three servings of meat weekly
- two or three servings of poultry weekly

Fish will provide the omega-3 fatty acids so important for the heart and the nervous system. Meat and poultry are excellent sources of iron and zinc, which are not as well absorbed from plant foods as they are from meats. And whole grains are rich in minerals and fibers, while beans, peas, and lentils are folate and mineral-rich, and an even better fiber source.

Navy Bean-Tomato Gratin

Servings: 6

A good way to use up extra zucchini and tomatoes! Substitute garlic powder for fresh garlic, canned tomatoes for fresh, if you wish.

2 tablespoons olive oil
1 cup celery, thinly sliced
1/2 cup red onion, thinly sliced
1 teaspoon garlic, minced
2 cups tomatoes, seeded and diced
2 cups zucchini, diced 1/4"
1/4 cup ripe pitted olives, sliced
1 teaspoon dried sage
2 (15 ounce) cans navy beans, rinsed

3/4 cup fresh whole-wheat bread crumbs
1/4 cup ground flax seed
1 teaspoon garlic, minced
1/4 cup parsley, chopped or 1 tablespoon dried parsley
2 tablespoons grated Parmesan
1 teaspoon lemon zest, grated

1. Preheat oven to 350 degrees F. Heat olive oil in heavy pot. Add celery, onions and garlic. Sauté over medium heat for 3 minutes. Add tomatoes and zucchini and simmer for 5 minutes. Remove from heat. Add olives and sage.

2. In blender or food processor, or with a hand masher, purée one cup of the beans; add puree and remaining beans to tomato mixture. Mix well and adjust seasoning with salt and pepper. Transfer to an oiled 2-quart shallow baking dish. Combine bread crumbs, flax seed, garlic, parsley, Parmesan cheese, and lemon zest in small bowl. Mix well and sprinkle evenly over casserole. Bake at 350 degrees F. until bubbly and golden, about 45 minutes. Let rest 5 or 10 minutes before serving.

What's great about this recipe ?			
"Easy-Fix"		"Bone Health"	✔
"Quick-Fix"		"Heart Health"	✔
"Easy-Chew"	✔	"Sweetie"	
"Hands-on"		"High Fiber"	✔

SuperSource: Vits.B1, C, folate, potassium, iron, magnesium, phosphorus, copper, chromium, fiber

Nutrition information per serving: 310 calories, 41 g carbohydrates, 15 g protein, 10 g fat, 2 g saturated fat, 1 mg cholesterol, 912 mg sodium, 11 g fiber. Good source of vits. B1, B3, B6, E, K, pant.acid, zinc.

Sunflower Warmer

Servings: 4

✓

This recipe has been one of our family's favorites for years. I use a food processor for chopping and mincing, and I often cook a large pot of brown rice ahead of time, then freeze it in one-cup portions; these shortcuts make the dish really quick-to-fix.* Note the SuperSource box – this one is a real winner! Many nuts are as delicious as sunflower seeds in this casserole – for example, pistachios, chopped macadamias, walnuts, or almonds – take your pick. They're all good for you, too!

2 large onions, chopped
8 ounces mushrooms, sliced
2 tablespoons peanut or olive oil
1/2 cup minced parsley
1 cup diced celery

1/4 teaspoon ground ginger, or 1/2 teaspoon fresh ginger, grated
1 cup sunflower seeds or other nuts
3 cups cooked brown rice, kept warm

1. Saute onions and mushrooms in oil.
2. Add celery, parsley and ginger. Cover and cook 10 minutes over low heat. Remove from stove.
3. Add seeds or nuts, and serve on a bed of cooked brown rice.

What's great about this recipe ?

"Easy-Fix"	✔*	"Bone Health"	✔
"Quick-Fix"	✔*	"Heart Health"	✔
"Easy-Chew"		"Sweetie"	
"Hands-on"		"High Fiber"	✔

SuperSource: Vits. B1, B2, 3, B6, E, folate, pant.acid, potassium, iron, magnesium, phosphorus, zinc, copper, manganese, selenium, chromium, fiber

Nutrition information per serving: 481 calories, 52 g carbohydrates, 14 g protein, 26 g fat, 3 g saturated fat, 0 mg cholesterol, 37 mg sodium, 9 g fiber. Good source of vit. C.

Chickpeas, Pasta, and Greens

Servings: 6

A one-pot meal – pasta, beans, vegetables, and cheese.

12 ounces pasta (spaghetti, ziti, or other shape) cooked al dente, drained
1 tablespoon olive oil
1 medium onion, chopped
3 cloves garlic, minced
1/4 teaspoon cayenne pepper
1/2 teaspoon dried thyme
1/2 teaspoon paprika
1/4 teaspoon turmeric

1 (15-ounce) can chickpeas, with liquid
2 cups chopped tomato
1/4 teaspoon black pepper
1 bunch (10-12 ounces) collard greens, kale, or chard, washed, stems removed, chopped
Cooking spray
3/4 cup grated Cheddar cheese

1. Preheat oven to 350 F. Add olive oil to large skillet and heat to medium. Saute onion, garlic, cayenne, thyme, paprika, and turmeric about 6-8 minutes, or until onions are translucent. Add chickpeas, 1/2 cup of the reserved liquid, tomatoes, and pepper. Lower heat and simmer 15 minutes, adding remaining chickpea liquid if mixture becomes dry. Add cooked pasta and toss lightly.
2. Place greens in a large pot with 2/3 cup water, bring to a boil, then lower heat to simmer, and cook until tender, about 15-30 minutes, depending on type of greens. Stir into chickpea mixture, tossing lightly.
3. Spray a 3-quart baking dish with cooking spray and spoon in the chickpea mixture. Cover pan and bake 20 minutes. Remove cover, scatter cheese over top, and bake, uncovered, 5 minutes, or til cheese is melted.

What's great about this recipe ?

"Easy-Fix"		"Bone Health"	✔
"Quick-Fix"		"Heart Health"	✔
"Easy-Chew"	✔	"Sweetie"	
"Hands-on"		"High Fiber"	✔

SuperSource: Vits.A, B1, B2, B3, B6, C, iron, phosphorus, copper, manganese, selenium, chromium, fiber

Nutrition information per serving: 403 calories, 65 g carbohydrates, 16 g protein, 9 g fat, 4 g saturated fat, 15 mg cholesterol, 411 mg sodium, 6 g fiber. Good source of vits. E, K, folate, pant. acid, potassium, calcium, magnesium, zinc.

Lentil Bake

Servings: 8

This dish is a nutritional powerhouse! Lentils and rice can be cooked and frozen ahead of time to speed preparation. Add a glass of fruit juice, sliced tomato, and whole-grain bread for a complete meal.

1 pound dry lentils, cooked (about 7 cups cooked lentils)	1 teaspoon ground black pepper
1 tablespoon honey	1/2 teaspoon ground ginger
1 tablespoon cider vinegar	1 cup chopped onion
3 tablespoons reduced-sodium soy sauce	1 cup sliced carrot
2 teaspoons dry mustard	1 cup sliced celery
	2 tablespoons peanut oil
	8 cups cooked brown rice

1. Rinse lentils, and cook in 5 cups water, about 45 minutes or until tender, adding water if lentils dry out. Place cooked lentils in 2 1/2-quart casserole.
2. Combine honey, vinegar, soy sauce, mustard, pepper and ginger in small bowl. Gently stir into lentils.
3. Cook and stir onion, carrot and celery in oil in large skillet over medium-high heat until onion is translucent. Add to lentils. Cover and bake at 350 degrees F 45 minutes. Uncover and bake 15 minutes more. Serve over rice. A serving is about one cup lentils over one cup rice.

What's great about this recipe ?

"Easy-Fix"		"Bone Health"	✔
"Quick-Fix"		"Heart Health"	✔
"Easy-Chew"	✔	"Sweetie"	
"Hands-on"		"High Fiber"	✔

SuperSource: Vits. A, B1, B3, B6, folate, pant.acid, potassium, iron, magnesium, phosphorus, zinc, copper, manganese, selenium, fiber

Nutrition information per serving: 470 calories, 85 g carbohydrates, 21 g protein, 6 g fat, 1 g saturated fat, 0 mg cholesterol, 251 mg sodium, 22 g fiber. Good source of vits.B2, chromium.

Kathrynne's Tostada

Servings: 2

If you favor Southwestern dishes, you'll enjoy this tostada. It makes a light main dish, and can be as mild or spicy as you like. It calls for quite a few ingredients, but it's easy to assemble, using any beans you choose – pinto, kidney, etc. Use ready-made guacamole to speed preparation.

Guacamole:
1 ripe avocado, peeled, seeded, and mashed
1 tablespoon lemon or lime juice
1 garlic clove, minced, or 1/4 teaspoon garlic powder
2 tablespoons red or sweet onion, minced
1/4 teaspoon crushed red pepper flakes (optional)
2 TB minced cilantro or parsley

2 (8-10") flour tortillas, lightly toasted
2 cups iceberg lettuce, chopped
1 (16 ounce) can reduced-sodium black beans, rinsed and drained
1 medium tomato, diced
2 ounces Cheddar cheese, grated
2 tablespoons sliced ripe olives
2 tablespoons sour cream
2 tablespoons salsa
sliced fresh or canned jalapenos (optional)

1. Fold together the mashed avocado, lemon juice, garlic, onion, crushed red pepper, and cilantro.
2. Place each toasted tortilla on a plate. Divide the chopped lettuce equally between the two tortillas. Follow with the beans, tomato, guacamole, and cheese.
3. Scatter olives over each tostada. Top with a tablespoon of sour cream and a tablespoon of salsa. Pass sliced jalapenos if desired.

What's great about this recipe ?			
"Easy-Fix"	✔	"Bone Health"	✔
"Quick-Fix"		"Heart Health"	
"Easy-Chew"		"Sweetie"	
"Hands-on"		"High Fiber"	✔

SuperSource: Vits. A, B2, C, K, folate, potassium, iron, copper, phosphorus, chromium, fiber

Nutrition information per serving: 543 calories, 63 g carbohydrates, 24 g protein, 29 g fat, 10 g saturated fat, 36 mg cholesterol, 684 mg sodium, 26 g fiber. Good source of vitamins B1, B3, B6, B12, E, pant. acid, biotin, calcium, magnesium, zinc, manganese.

Pat's Own Easy Cheese-y Spinach Casserole

Servings: 4

Be sure to use well-chopped spinach, so this will be easier to chew. It's protein-rich, which is good, but take Sinemet at least 30 minutes before this meal.

2 cups low-fat low-sodium cottage cheese
3 eggs, slightly beaten
4 ounces Cheddar or Monterey Jack cheese, grated
1 teaspoon olive oil

1 (10 ounce) package frozen chopped spinach, partly thawed, cut or chopped in 1" pieces
3 tablespoons flour
1 1/2 tablespoons ground flax seed

1. Preheat oven to 350 degrees F. Grease a 1 1/2 quart shallow baking dish.
2. Combine cottage cheese and eggs. Stir in cheese and oil. Stir in the pieces of frozen spinach, flour, and flax seed.
3. Bake at 350 degrees F. for about one hour, or til set.

What's great about this recipe ?			
"Easy-Fix"	✔	"Bone Health"	✔
"Quick-Fix"		"Heart Health"	
"Easy-Chew"	✔	"Sweetie"	
"Hands-on"		"High Fiber"	

SuperSource: Vits.A, B2, B12, K, folate, biotin, iron, calcium, phosphorus, copper, manganese, selenium

Nutrition information per serving: 315 calories, 13 g carbohydrates, 29 g protein, 17 g fat, 8 g saturated fat, 194 mg cholesterol, 391 mg sodium, 3 g fiber. Good source of vitamins B1, B6, E, pant.acid, potassium, magnesium, zinc, chromium, fiber.

Three Beans and Noodles

Servings: 6

Served at room temperature, this resembles a salad but is a hearty main dish. Leftovers taste just as good the next day. Reprinted courtesy of the National Pasta Association.

1 pound medium or wide egg noodles, uncooked
1 15-ounce can kidney beans, rinsed and drained
1 15-ounce can chickpeas, rinsed and drained
1 cup frozen green beans, thawed
1 small red onion, chopped
1 red bell pepper, seeds and ribs removed, chopped
3 tablespoons Dijon mustard
2 tablespoons sunflower oil
3 tablespoons red wine vinegar
3 tablespoons chopped fresh parsley

1. Prepare noodles according to package directions; drain. Rinse under cold water and drain again.
2. In a large bowl, stir together the noodles, kidney beans, chickpeas, green beans, onion and bell pepper. In a small bowl, stir together mustard, oil, vinegar, and parsley. Toss pasta-bean mixture with dressing and serve.

What's great about this recipe ?

"Easy-Fix"	✔	"Bone Health"	✔
"Quick-Fix"	✔	"Heart Health"	✔
"Easy-Chew"		"Sweetie"	
"Hands-on"		"High Fiber"	✔

SuperSource: Vits. B1, B2, B3, B6, C, folate, iron, zinc, phosphorus, copper, manganese, selenium, fiber

Nutrition information per serving: 570 calories, 89 g carbohydrates, 22 g protein, 15 g fat, 3 g saturated fat, 72 mg cholesterol, 275 mg sodium, 12 g fiber. Good source of vits. B12, E, pant.acid, potassium, magnesium, chromium.

Savory Rice and Cheese Bake

Servings: 4

A food processor makes short work of chopping the vegetables while the rice cooks. To lower the sodium content, use reduced-sodium cottage cheese.

1 1/2 cups brown rice
1/4 teaspoon salt
1 large onion, chopped (1 cup)
3/4 cup shredded carrot
3/4 cup diced celery
1 tablespoon olive oil
1 1/2 cups lowfat cottage cheese
2 tablespoons chopped pimiento

1 large egg
1 tablespoon minced parsley
1/2 teaspoon rosemary, crumbled
3 tablespoons ground flax seed
1/4 teaspoon black pepper, ground
2 ounces Cheddar cheese, grated
2 tablespoons sesame seeds

1. Preheat oven to 375 F.
2. Rinse rice. Place in saucepan with water and salt. Bring to a boil, reduce heat, and simmer for 30 - 45 minutes, depending on type of rice.
3. Meantime, saute onion, carrot and celery in oil til tender, about 3 minutes.
4. Mix together cooked rice, onion mixture, cottage cheese, pimiento, egg, parsley, rosemary, flax seed, and pepper.
5. Spoon mixture into two-quart casserole dish, top with grated cheese and sesame seeds.
6. Cover dish, and bake 25 minutes.

What's great about this recipe ?

"Easy-Fix"	✔	"Bone Health"	✔
"Quick-Fix"		"Heart Health"	✔
"Easy-Chew"	✔	"Sweetie"	
"Hands-on"		"High Fiber"	

SuperSource: Vits. A, B1, B2, B3, B6, B12, pant.acid, iron, magnesium, phosphorus, zinc, copper, manganese, selenium, chromium

Nutrition information per serving: 519 calories, 66 g carbohydrates, 25 g protein, 17 g fat, 5 g saturated fat, 72 mg cholesterol, 645 mg sodium, 6 g fiber. Good source of vits. C, E, folate, biotin, potassium, calcium, fiber.

Quelites (Spinach With Beans)

Servings: 4

This Mexican dish is a good light entree, but would also be wonderful served with rice or enchiladas, or hot quesadillas. You'll want some warm corn tortillas to soak up the remaining sauce, it's delicious!

1 tablespoon olive oil
3 tablespoons chopped onion
1 minced jalapeno pepper (optional)
1 (15 ounce) can reduced-sodium white beans (navy or Great Northern), with liquid

1 teaspoon chili powder
1 1/2 lb fresh spinach, washed & chopped, or 10 ounces frozen, thawed spinach
1 hard-cooked egg, sliced
12 corn tortillas, warmed

1. In large deep skillet, heat olive oil over medium heat. Add onion and jalapeno and cook till tender, about 2-3 minutes. Add beans and chili powder, stirring well. Add the spinach by handfuls, stirring until it wilts before adding another handful. Simmer for 4-5 minutes to let flavors blend.
2. Spoon into serving dish. Garnish with egg slices. Serve with warm tortillas. If desired, pass bowls of avocado, chopped sweet onion, grated cheese, or your own favorites, as toppings.

What's great about this recipe ?

"Easy-Fix"	✔	"Bone Health"	✔
"Quick-Fix"	✔	"Heart Health"	✔
"Easy-Chew"	✔	"Sweetie"	
"Hands-on"		"High Fiber"	✔

SuperSource: Vits. A, B1, B2, B6, C, E, K, folate, biotin, potassium, iron, magnesium, phosphorus, copper, manganese, chromium, fiber

Nutrition information per serving: 382 calories, 65 g carbohydrates, 19 g protein, 8 g fat, 1 g saturated fat, 53 mg cholesterol, 550 mg sodium, 15 g fiber. Good source of vits. B3, pant. acid, calcium, zinc, selenium.

Black Beans and Yellow Rice

Servings: 4

Vary ingredients: try adding, or garnishing with, jalapeno, avocado, green onions, cilantro, to suit your taste.

3 tablespoons peanut oil
1 small onion, chopped
1 clove garlic, minced
1/4 teaspoon turmeric
1/2 teaspoon ground cumin
1/2 teaspoon salt
1/4 teaspoon black pepper
1 1/2 cups long-grain brown rice
3 cups water

1 chicken bouillon cube
1 (15-ounce) can, black beans, drained and rinsed
1 green bell pepper, chopped
1 tomato, diced
1 tablespoon red wine vinegar
1/4 cup fresh parsley, chopped
1 lime, quartered, for serving (optional)

1. In a medium saucepan, heat 2 tablespoons oil over moderately low heat. Add onion and cook, stirring occasionally, until translucent, about 5 minutes. Stir in the garlic, turmeric, cumin, 1/4 teaspoon salt, black pepper, and rice. Cook, stirring frequently, for 2 minutes.
2. Add the water and bouillon cube; bring to a boil. Reduce heat to low and simmer, covered, until liquid is absorbed and the rice is tender, about 25-35 minutes.
3. In large bowl, combine beans, bell pepper, and tomatoes. Add the remaining 1 tablespoon oil and 1/4 teaspoon salt, the vinegar, and parsley. Toss gently to combine.
4. Spoon cooked rice into serving dish. Spoon bean mixture over. Serve with lime wedges, if using.

What's great about this recipe ?

"Easy-Fix"		"Bone Health"	✔
"Quick-Fix"		"Heart Health"	✔
"Easy-Chew"	✔	"Sweetie"	
"Hands-on"		"High Fiber"	✔

SuperSource: Vits. B1, B3, B6, C pant.acid, iron, magnesium, phosphorus, copper, manganese, selenium, fiber

Nutrition information per serving: 442 calories, 76 g carbohydrates, 11 g protein, 12 g fat, 2 g saturated fat, 0 mg cholesterol, 491 mg sodium, 10 g fiber. Good source of vits. E, potassium, zinc, chromium.

Layered Bean Lasagna
Servings: 4

You can substitute garlic powder for fresh garlic, and packaged shredded Mozzarella, to speed preparation time. Reprinted courtesy of Ontario White Bean Producers.

1 tablespoon peanut oil
1 cup chopped onion
2 cloves garlic, minced
1 (7 1/2-ounce) can tomato sauce
1 teaspoon dried oregano
1 teaspoon dried basil
1 (14-ounce) can reduced-sodium small white beans, undrained

1 cup reduced-sodium cottage cheese
1 1/2 cups grated Mozzarella cheese, divided
1 10-ounce can mushroom pieces, drained
1 egg, beaten
3 cups cooked, drained, egg noodles

1. In a medium skillet heat oil over medium heat: add onion and garlic. Sauté until softened. Add tomato sauce, oregano, basil and beans; bring to boil. Reduce heat and simmer uncovered 8-10 minutes.
2. In a small bowl combine cottage cheese, 1 cup (250 milliliter) Mozzarella cheese, mushrooms, and egg; mix well.
3. In a greased 9-inch square (1.5 liter) baking dish, place one-half of the noodles; top with half the cheese mixture and half the bean mixture. Repeat layers and sprinkle remaining cheese on top. Bake in 325 degrees F. (160 degrees C) oven 40-45 minutes or until heated through.

What's great about this recipe ?

"Easy-Fix"	✔	"Bone Health"	✔
"Quick-Fix"		"Heart Health"	✔
"Easy-Chew"	✔	"Sweetie"	
"Hands-on"		"High Fiber"	✔

SuperSource: Vits. B1, B2, B3, B6, folate, pant.acid, potassium, iron, calcium, magnesium, phosphorus, zinc, copper, manganese, selenium, chromium, fiber

Nutrition information per serving: 566 calories, 72 g carbohydrates, 36 g protein, 17 g fat, 7 g saturated fat, 118 mg cholesterol, 798 mg sodium, 11 g fiber. Good source of Vits. A, B12, C, E, K.

Tomato-Black Bean-Rice Plate

Servings: 8

This is close to, but not quite, a soup or stew, and absolutely delectable! Use your favorite canned beans, if you don't care for black beans. Using cooking spray makes cleanup easier.

Cooking spray
1 tablespoon olive oil
1 cup chopped onion
3/4 cup chopped bell pepper
2 cups reduced-sodium tomato juice
1 cup water
3 (15 ounce) cans black beans, rinsed and drained
1 (14 ounce) can reduced-sodium whole tomatoes, undrained, chopped

1 (8 ounce) can reduced-sodium tomato sauce
1 (4 ounce) jar diced pimiento, drained
1 teaspoon pepper
1 clove garlic or 1/2 teaspoon garlic powder
1/4 teaspoon salt
4 cups cooked brown rice
1 cup (4 ounces) shredded Monterey Jack cheese

1. Coat large Dutch oven with cooking spray. Add oil. Place over medium-high heat til hot. Add onion & pepper; saute til tender, about 3-5 minutes. Add tomato juice, water, beans, tomatoes, tomato sauce, pimientos, pepper, garlic, and salt; bring to boil. Cover, reduce heat, simmer 20-25 minutes to blend flavors and thicken slightly.
2. To serve, place 1/2 cup rice in each of 8 individual bowls. Ladle 1 cup beans over each serving. Sprinkle with 2 TB cheese.

What's great about this recipe ?

"Easy-Fix"	✔	"Bone Health"	✔
"Quick-Fix"		"Heart Health"	✔
"Easy-Chew"	✔	"Sweetie"	
"Hands-on"		"High Fiber"	✔

SuperSource: Vits. B6, C, potassium, iron, phosphorus, copper, manganese, selenium, fiber

Nutrition information per serving: 310 calories, 55 g carbohydrates, 14 g protein, 7 g fat, 3 g saturated fat, 13 mg cholesterol, 498 mg sodium, 12 g fiber. Good source of vits. A, B1, B2, B3, K, pant.acid, calcium, magnesium, zinc, chromium.

Alison's Soybean Casserole

Servings: 4

This is a truly "super" recipe. If your family likes it, I'd recommend serving it several times a month. You can use canned soybeans for convenience.

Cooking spray
1 cup dry egg noodles, cooked and drained
3 cups cooked soybeans or canned soybeans
1 (15 ounce) can reduced-sodium tomatoes, undrained, chopped
1/4 teaspoon salt
1/2 teaspoon pepper
1/2 teaspoon dried oregano

1/2 teaspoon dried basil
1 teaspoon dried parsley
1 cup sliced green onions or chopped sweet onion
1 cup plain yogurt
4 ounces cream cheese, cut in ½" cubes
1/2 cup dry bread crumbs
1/4 cup grated Parmesan cheese
1/4 cup wheat germ

1. Preheat oven to 350 degrees F. Spray a 3 quart baking dish with cooking spray.
2. Combine cooked noodles, soybeans, tomatoes, salt, pepper, oregano, basil, parsley, green onions, yogurt and cream cheese cubes; spoon into baking dish.
3. Combine bread crumbs, Parmesan cheese, and wheat germ. Sprinkle evenly over top of mixture. Bake 30 minutes or till bubbly.

What's great about this recipe ?

"Easy-Fix"	✔	"Bone Health"	✔
"Quick-Fix"		"Heart Health"	✔
"Easy-Chew"	✔	"Sweetie"	
"Hands-on"		"High Fiber"	✔

SuperSource: Vits. B1, B2, B6, folate, E, K, potassium, iron, magnesium, phosphorus, zinc, copper, manganese, fiber

Nutrition information per serving: 498 calories, 44 g carbohydrates, 33 g protein, 23 g fat, 8 g saturated fat, 41 mg cholesterol, 412 mg sodium, 11 g fiber. Good source of vits. A, B3, B12, C, pant.acid, biotin, calcium, selenium, chromium.

Salmon Potato Cakes

Servings: 6

Salmon is a superfood. It's a terrific source of omega-3 fatty acids, and canned salmon contains soft, digestible bones that boost our calcium intake. To speed preparation, microwave the potatoes, chop 1/2", and mash (include the skins to increase fiber and nutrients). Reprinted courtesy of Alaska Seafood Marketing Institute

1 (14 3/4-ounce) can no-added-salt salmon
2 1/2 cups prepared mashed potatoes
1 egg
1 tablespoon chopped parsley
1/2 cup sliced green onions
Cooking spray

1 cup toasted wheat germ
Horseradish-dill sauce:
1/2 cup mayonnaise
1/2 cup lowfat plain yogurt
1 tablespoon prepared horseradish
1/4 teaspoon dill weed
Black pepper, to taste

1. Drain salmon and break into chunks, including bones. Set aside.
2. Mix potatoes with egg and parsley until smooth and well combined. Gently fold in salmon and green onions.
3. Spray a large skillet with cooking spray and heat over medium high heat.
4. Form mixture into 1/4 cup patties, coat with wheat germ and fry 2 to 3 minutes on each side, or until golden brown. Serve with Horseradish-Dill Sauce.
5. Horseradish-Dill Sauce: Whisk together all ingredients until combined.

What's great about this recipe ?

"Easy-Fix"	✔	"Bone Health"	✔
"Quick-Fix"	✔	"Heart Health"	✔
"Easy-Chew"	✔	"Sweetie"	
"Hands-on"		"High Fiber"	

SuperSource: Vits. B1, E, K, iron, phosphorus, zinc, copper, manganese, chromium

Nutrition information per serving: 434 calories, 28 g carbohydrates, 24 g protein, 26 g fat, 6 g saturated fat, 99 mg cholesterol, 716 mg sodium, 5 g fiber. Good source of vitamins B2, B3, B6, C, folate, pant.acid, potassium, calcium, magnesium, fiber.

Shrimp Scampi Dijon
Servings: 4

Delicious any time! Buy frozen peeled, deveined shrimp to speed preparation. You can also used bottled minced garlic, and in a pinch, dried parsley.* Although the dish is high in fat, it's mostly heart-protective fat; and it's a tasty way to get selenium, an antioxidant that pairs with vitamin E. The linguine will soak up the delicious sauce; but it's a good idea to serve with crusty bread to sop up any that remains!

1/4 cup dry white wine or chicken broth
1 tablespoon lemon juice
1 teaspoon Dijon mustard
1/4 cup olive oil
1 tablespoon butter
1 tablespoon minced garlic, or to taste

2 pounds fresh or frozen shrimp, peeled and deveined; thawed, if frozen
1/4 teaspoon crushed red pepper flakes (optional)
Minced fresh parsley, for garnish
8 ounces linguine, cooked and drained

1. Stir together wine, lemon juice and mustard. Set aside.
2. Set 10" skillet over medium heat, add oil and butter and heat till it shimmers. Saute garlic until just golden. Add wine mixture and heat, about 30 seconds. Add shrimp and cook 3-5 minutes, or until opaque. Season with red pepper, and garnish with parsley. Serve over hot cooked linguine.

What's great about this recipe ?			
"Easy-Fix"	✔	"Bone Health"	✔
"Quick-Fix"	✔*	"Heart Health"	
"Easy-Chew"		"Sweetie"	
"Hands-on"		"High Fiber"	

SuperSource: Vits. B1, B2, B3, B12, iron, magnesium, phosphorus, zinc, copper, selenium

Nutrition information per serving: 594 calories, 43 g carbohydrates, 55 g protein, 20 g fat, 5 g saturated fat, 451 mg cholesterol, 551 mg sodium, 1 g fiber. Good source of vits. A, E, B6, pant.acid, potassium, manganese.

Salmon Bake With Pecan Crunch Coating

Servings: 4

This recipe is good enough to be a "special occasion" dish – even children love it! Yet it's rich in omega-3 fats, so your heart will love it too. Get the freshest salmon you can find. Drop a piece of whole-grain bread into a blender or food processor to make fresh crumbs; then process the pecans, then the fresh parsley, scraping out the bowl after each item.* Reprinted courtesy of Alaska Seafood Marketing Institute.

2 tablespoons Dijon mustard
2 tablespoons butter, melted
4 teaspoons honey
1/4 cup fresh whole-wheat bread crumbs (about 1/2 slice)
1/4 cup pecans, finely chopped (or walnuts)

2 teaspoons minced parsley
4 (4 ounce) salmon fillets, or steaks
1/4 teaspoon salt
1/4 teaspoon black pepper
1 lemon, cut in wedges

1. Preheat oven to 400 degrees F. Mix together mustard, butter and honey in a small bowl; set aside.
2. Mix together breadcrumbs, pecans and parsley in a small bowl; set aside.
3. Season each salmon fillet or steak with salt and pepper. Place on a lightly greased baking sheet or broiling pan. Brush each fillet or steak with mustard-honey mixture. Pat top of each fillet or steak with breadcrumb mixture.
4. Bake for 10 minutes per inch of thickness, measured at thickest part, or until salmon just flakes when tested with a fork. Serve with lemon wedges. Makes 4 servings.

What's great about this recipe ?

"Easy-Fix"	✔*	"Bone Health"	✔
"Quick-Fix"	✔*	"Heart Health"	✔
"Easy-Chew"	✔	"Sweetie"	
"Hands-on"		"High Fiber"	

SuperSource: Vits. B1, B2, B3, B6, B12, pant.acid, phosphorus, copper

Nutrition information per serving: 304 calories, 12 g carbohydrates, 24 g protein, 19 g fat, 5 g saturated fat, 79 mg cholesterol, 318 mg sodium, 2 g fiber. Good source of vit. C, potassium, iron, magnesium, zinc, manganese, chromium.

Asian-style Alaska Pollock

Servings: 4

Cod, haddock, or other white fish will work also. To toast the sesame seeds, heat a small skillet to medium; add seeds, and toast, stirring frequently, 2-3 minutes, or till fragrant and lightly browned. If chewing is difficult, omit green onions and seeds. Reprinted courtesy of the Alaska Seafood Marketing Institute.

1 pound pollock fillets, thawed if necessary
2 tablespoons dry white wine or chicken broth
2 tablespoons low-sodium soy sauce
1 teaspoon peanut or safflower oil
1 teaspoon fresh ginger, minced; or 1/2 teaspoon ground ginger

1 clove garlic, minced
1/2 teaspoon cornstarch
1/3 cup green onion, diagonally sliced
1 tablespoon sesame seeds, toasted
1 fresh lemon, wedged

1. Place pollock fillets in shallow heat-proof dish or pie dish. Combine wine, soy sauce, oil, ginger, garlic and cornstarch; spoon over fillets.
2. Place vegetable steamer in large skillet or wok; add water to depth of 1 inch. Bring water to boil. Top pollock with green onion; place dish of fillets on rack. Cover skillet and return water to boil.
3. Steam fillets allowing about 10 minutes cooking time per inch of thickness measured at its thickest part or until fish flakes easily when tested with a fork. Garnish with sesame seeds. Serve with lemon wedges.

What's great about this recipe ?			
"Easy-Fix"	✔	"Bone Health"	✔
"Quick-Fix"	✔	"Heart Health"	✔
"Easy-Chew"	✔	"Sweetie"	
"Hands-on"		"High Fiber"	

SuperSource: Vits. B12, C, phosphorus, selenium

Nutrition information per serving: 143 calories, 6 g carbohydrates, 22 g protein, 4 g fat, 1 g saturated fat, 49 mg cholesterol, 364 mg sodium, 2 g fiber. Good source of vits. B1, B3, B6, potassium, iron, magnesium, copper.

Baked Sole

Servings: 4

Any white fish, such as halibut, perch, cod, pollack, and rockfish, will work equally well. Good with pasta tossed with olive oil, lemon juice, basil, and chopped tomato.

1/4 cup grated Parmesan cheese
1/2 cup parsley, minced, or 2 TB dried parsley
1/2 cup dry bread crumbs
1/4 cup wheat germ
1/4 cup ground flax seed
1 clove garlic, minced, or ½ teaspoon garlic powder
1 teaspoon lemon zest

1/4 teaspoon salt
1/4 teaspoon pepper
1 pound sole fillets (can also use halibut or other white fish), thawed if frozen
1 tablespoon olive oil
Cooking spray
4 tablespoons sliced almonds
1 lemon, cut in wedges

1. Preheat oven to 325 degrees F. Mix together Parmesan, parsley, crumbs, wheat germ, flax seed, garlic, lemon zest, salt, and pepper on a plate.
2. Rinse fillets and pat dry on paper towel. Brush fillets with oil and dip both sides in bread crumb mixture.
3. Spray a baking pan with cooking spray, and place fillets in pan. Cover with any remaining crumb mixture. Sprinkle with almonds.
4. Bake uncovered at 325 degrees F for 15-20 minutes and check for doneness. Fish should flake when tested with fork. Serve with lemon wedges.

What's great about this recipe ?			
"Easy-Fix"	✔	"Bone Health"	✔
"Quick-Fix"	✔	"Heart Health"	✔
"Easy-Chew"	✔	"Sweetie"	
"Hands-on"		"High Fiber"	

SuperSource: Vits.B1, B12, C, E, iron, magnesium, phosphorus, copper, manganese

Nutrition information per serving: 304 calories, 20 g carbohydrates, 28 g protein, 13 g fat, 2 g saturated fat, 57 mg cholesterol, 446 mg sodium, 5 g fiber. Good source of vits. B2, B3, B6, folate, pant. acid, potassium, calcium, zinc, fiber.

Basic Best Salmon Loaf

Servings: 6

These can be made two ways – a single large loaf, to serve a group; or two smaller loaves, one of which can be frozen unbaked for later. Reprinted courtesy of the Alaska Seafood Marketing Institute.

1 (15-ounce) can salmon, including bones (mash bones)
1 1/2 cups soft whole-wheat bread crumbs (3 slices bread)
1/2 cup wheat germ
1/3 cup finely minced onions

1/4 cup skim or 1% milk
2 eggs
2 tablespoons chopped parsley
1 tablespoon lemon juice
1/4 teaspoon dill weed
1 dash black pepper

1. Drain and flake salmon, reserving 2 tablespoons liquid. Combine flaked salmon and reserved liquid with remaining ingredients.
2. Place in well-greased 8 1/2" × 4 1/2" × 2 1/2" loaf pan or two 6" x 3 1/2" x 2 1/4"pans (cover one pan tightly with aluminum foil, label it with the date, freeze). Bake large loaf at 350ºF for 45 minutes; 35-40 minutes for the smaller loaf; 45-55 minutes for the smaller loaf if frozen.

What's great about this recipe ?

"Easy-Fix"	✔	"Bone Health"	✔
"Quick-Fix"		"Heart Health"	✔
"Easy-Chew"	✔	"Sweetie"	
"Hands-on"		"High Fiber"	

SuperSource: Vits. B3, B12, D, biotin, iron, phosphorus, manganese, selenium, chromium

Nutrition information per serving: 201 calories, 13 g carbohydrates, 20 g protein, 7 g fat, 2 g saturated fat, 110 mg cholesterol, 538 mg sodium, 3 g fiber. Good source of vits. B1, B2, B6, K, folate, pant.acid, potassium, calcium, magnesium, zinc, copper, fiber.

Baked Tilapia In Basil Sauce

Servings: 6

Tilapia is a delicious mild fish that adapts very well to baking, broiling, and frying, and can take on many different flavorings. Reprinted courtesy of the American Tilapia Association.

1/2 cup celery, chopped	1/4 teaspoon pepper
1/2 cup onion, chopped	1 teaspoon fresh or dried tarragon
1/2 cup sweet red pepper, chopped	1 teaspoon fresh basil
3 tablespoons butter or margarine	1/4 cup 1% milk
3 tablespoons flour	1 cup Mozzarella cheese, shredded
1/2 teaspoon salt	1 1/2 pounds tilapia fillets

1. Preheat oven to 425 degrees F. In a medium skillet, sauté the celery, onions and sweet red pepper in butter or margarine until tender. Add the flour, salt, pepper, tarragon, basil and milk; mix well. Cook for 1 minute, stirring constantly until thickened. Add the cheese and stir until melted. Do not boil.

2. Rinse the tilapia fillets in cold water and drain thoroughly. Place the fish in a 12" × 8" × 2" baking dish; spoon the sauce evenly over the fish. Bake at 425° for 8 to 10 minutes or until the fish flakes easily when tested with a fork.

What's great about this recipe ?

"Easy-Fix"		"Bone Health"	✔
"Quick-Fix"		"Heart Health"	✔
"Easy-Chew"	✔	"Sweetie"	
"Hands-on"		"High Fiber"	

SuperSource: Phosphorus

Nutrition information per serving: 238 calories, 6 g carbohydrates, 28 g protein, 11 g fat, 6 g saturated fat, 28 mg cholesterol, 394 mg sodium, 1 g fiber. Good source of vits. A, B3, C, potassium, iron, calcium, chromium,.

Roasted Tilapia With Tomatoes and Olives

Servings: 6

Red snapper or cod would also work well in this dish. Reprinted courtesy of the American Tilapia Association.

Cooking spray

3 tablespoons extra-virgin olive oil

4 sprigs fresh thyme, minced, or 1 teaspoon dried thyme

3 tomatoes, peeled, seeded and chopped, or 1 (15 ounce) can tomatoes, chopped

3 tablespoons ground flax seed

1/2 cup coarsely chopped green olives

1/4 teaspoon dried hot red pepper flakes

2 garlic cloves, minced

1/2 cup finely chopped red onion

1 tablespoon fresh lime juice

1. Preheat the oven to 400 degrees F.
2. Spray with cooking spray a shallow baking dish large enough to hold the fillets in one layer.
3. In a bowl stir together the oil, thyme, tomatoes, flax seed, olives, red pepper flakes, garlic, onion, and lime juice. In the prepared baking dish arrange the fillets, skin sides down, and spoon the tomato mixture over them. Bake the fish, uncovered, in the middle of the oven 15 to 20 minutes, or until it just flakes.

What's great about this recipe ?

"Easy-Fix"	✔	"Bone Health"	✔
"Quick-Fix"	✔	"Heart Health"	✔
"Easy-Chew"	✔	"Sweetie"	
"Hands-on"		"High Fiber"	

SuperSource: Phosphorus

Nutrition information per serving: 226 calories, 7 g carbohydrates, 24 g protein, 12 g fat, 1 g saturated fat, 0 mg cholesterol, 340 mg sodium, 2 g fiber. Good source of vits. B3, C, E, K, potassium, iron, copper, manganese, chromium.

Pan-Fried Oysters

Servings: 2

Oysters are a superfood – they are a wealth of selenium, zinc, and vitamin B12, all very important to the health of those with PD.

1/2 cup flour
1/4 teaspoon black pepper
3 eggs, slightly beaten
1 tablespoon water
1/2 cup dry whole-wheat bread crumbs, fine

8 ounces fresh medium oysters, shucked
2 tablespoons peanut oil
1/4 cups seafood cocktail sauce (your favorite)
1 lemon, quartered

1. Heat oil in large cast iron or heavy skillet over medium heat.
2. Meantime, mix flour and pepper in a flat dish. Mix eggs and water in separate dish. Place bread crumbs in third dish. Dip each oyster in flour then egg/water mixture, then bread crumbs before putting in skillet. Cook approximately 3 minutes per side. Oysters should be medium brown color. Turn only once. Serve hot with cocktail sauce and lemon wedges.

What's great about this recipe ?			
"Easy-Fix"	✔	"Bone Health"	✔
"Quick-Fix"	✔	"Heart Health"	
"Easy-Chew"	✔	"Sweetie"	
"Hands-on"		"High Fiber"	

SuperSource: Vits, A, B1, B2, B12, C, K, pant.acid, biotin, iron, phosphorus, zinc, copper, manganese, selenium, chromium

Nutrition information per serving: 483 calories, 49 g carbohydrates, 21 g protein, 24 g fat, 5 g saturated fat, 346 mg cholesterol, 820 mg sodium, 5 g fiber. Good source of vits. B3, B6, E, folate, potassium, magnesium, fiber.

Blackened Catfish Fillets

Servings: 4

Fillets of catfish are a wonderful convenience food – no bones to deal with, quick-cooking, and great taste. Don't forget the lemon juice – it has more vitamin C than orange juice, plus some calcium as well!

1 tablespoon paprika	1/2 teaspoon oregano
1 tablespoon onion powder	1/4 teaspoon salt
1 teaspoon garlic powder	2 tablespoons butter, melted
1 teaspoon cayenne pepper	3 tablespoons olive oil
3/4 teaspoon white pepper	4 (4 ounce) catfish fillets
3/4 teaspoon black pepper	Cooking spray
1/2 teaspoon thyme	1 lemon cut in 4 wedges

1. Heat a large, heavy skillet over high heat for 10 minutes.
2. Mix paprika thru salt in a small bowl. Combine melted butter with 2 tablespoons olive oil in a shallow dish. Brush fillets on both sides with butter mixture, then sprinkle with the seasoning mixture.
3. Spray skillet with cooking spray. Add remaining 1 tablespoon olive oil to skillet and heat to medium-hot. Place fillets in the hot skillet and cook for 2 to 3 minutes on each side, or until blackened and fish flakes easily when tested with a fork. Serve with a squeeze of fresh lemon juice.

What's great about this recipe ?

"Easy-Fix"	✔	"Bone Health"	
"Quick-Fix"	✔	"Heart Health"	✔
"Easy-Chew"	✔	"Sweetie"	
"Hands-on"		"High Fiber"	

SuperSource: Vits. B1, B12, phosphorus

Nutrition information per serving: 306 calories, 4 g carbohydrates, 18 g protein, 25 g fat, 7 g saturated fat, 69 mg cholesterol, 267 mg sodium, 2 g fiber. Good source of vits. A, B3, B6, C, E, pant.acid, potassium, iron, copper.

Halibut Gypsy Style

Servings: 6

Use a food processor to make short work of the slicing, and this will become an "Easy-Fix" recipe.* For those who have difficulty chewing, chop the onion, potato, and tomato instead of slicing.* Reprinted courtesy of the California Seafood Council.

1 pound potatoes, thinly sliced
2 large onions, thinly sliced
1 1/2 pounds halibut fillet
2 large tomatoes, thinly sliced
2 cloves garlic, minced or pressed
1 cup white wine or water
1/4 cup parsley, finely chopped

1 bay leaf
2 tablespoons olive oil
1/4 teaspoon salt and pepper
Zest of 1/2 lemon
Lemon wedges
Parsley sprigs

1. In casserole dish, layer potatoes, onions, and fish, adding tomatoes to last layer. Mix together garlic, wine, parsley, bay leaf, olive oil, salt, pepper, and lemon zest. Pour over casserole, adding water if more liquid is needed.
2. Cover tightly, bake at 325 degrees F for 30-40 minutes, or until cooked. Check for liquid halfway through cooking time. Serve with lemon wedges, garnished with parsley sprigs.

What's great about this recipe ?

"Easy-Fix"	✔*	"Bone Health"	✔
"Quick-Fix"		"Heart Health"	✔
"Easy-Chew"	✔*	"Sweetie"	
"Hands-on"		"High Fiber"	

SuperSource: Vits. B3, B6, B12, C, potassium, iron, magnesium, phosphorus, copper, manganese, chromium

Nutrition information per serving: 283 calories, 23 g carbohydrates, 27 g protein, 7 g fat, 1 g saturated fat, 36 mg cholesterol, 173 mg sodium, 4 g fiber. Good source of vits. A, B1, B2, E, folate, pant.acid, biotin, fiber.

Carribean Fish Fillet With Rum

Servings: 6

Mince shallots and garlic in a blender or food processor to hurry-up the dish. This should ideally be served with pasta or cooked rice, or crusty bread, to soak up the wonderful sauce. Red snapper, catfish, mahi mahi, halibut, salmon or grouper are all good choices.

1 ½ pounds fish fillet, 3/4" thick, skin and bones removed
4 shallots, peeled and minced
4 cloves garlic, peeled and minced
1 cup calcium-fortified orange juice
1 cup white wine
1/4 cup dark rum

Juice of 2 limes
1/4 cup reduced sodium soy sauce
1/4 cup parsley, chopped
1/4 teaspoon white pepper
1/4 teaspoon salt
2 tablespoons fresh rosemary, chopped

1. Wash fillet and pat dry with paper towels.
2. In nonreactive dish, combine shallot, garlic, orange juice, wine, rum, lime juice, soy sauce, parsley, pepper, salt, and rosemary. Add fillet, turning to coat. Marinate 30 minutes in refrigerator. Remove fillet, removing marinade to saucepan.
3. Boil down marinade till it is reduced by half. Keep warm.
4. Broil or grill fillet for 3 to 4 minutes on a side, depending on thickness, turning gently. The fish should still be slightly translucent in the center since it will continue to cook after being removed from heat.
5. Remove fillet to serving dish, spoon marinade over fish. Serve immediately.

What's great about this recipe ?

"Easy-Fix"	✔	"Bone Health"	✔
"Quick-Fix"		"Heart Health"	✔
"Easy-Chew"	✔	"Sweetie"	
"Hands-on"		"High Fiber"	

SuperSource: Vits, B6, B12, phosphorus, selenium

Nutrition information per serving: 219 calories, 9 g carbohydrates, 24 g protein, 2 g fat, 0 g saturated fat, 42 mg cholesterol, 477 mg sodium, 1 g fiber. Good source of vit. C, pantothenic acid, potassium, iron, magnesium, manganese.

Halibut Domenica

Servings: 6

Wine, mushrooms, and cheese flavor this wonderful baked fish. Reprinted courtesy of Alaska Seafood Marketing Institute.

1 1/2 pounds halibut fillets
1/2 cup dry white wine (or chicken broth)
1 tablespoon lemon juice
1/2 pound mushrooms, thinly sliced
1/2 medium onion, chopped
1/4 teaspoon thyme
2 tablespoons olive oil

2 tablespoons butter
4 tablespoons flour
1 cup fish liquid
1 cup skim or 1% milk, or milk substitute
1 cup shredded Monterey Jack cheese
paprika or dill weed

1. Preheat oven to 400 degrees. Arrange halibut in a shallow baking dish. Pour wine (or broth) and lemon juice over fish. Cover and bake in a 400° oven for about 10 minutes. Let cool slightly. Drain fish liquid into a measuring cup. Add enough wine or water to make one cup of liquid.
2. Sauce: In skillet, sauté mushrooms, onions and thyme in olive oil. Remove from skillet and reserve. In same skillet, melt butter and blend 4 tablespoons flour to make a roux. On low heat, gradually blend in 1 cup of fish liquid and 1 cup of milk. Bring to boil, stirring constantly, and cook 1 or 2 minutes until thickened. Remove from heat, add mushroom mixture. Let cool.
3. Spoon sauce over halibut, covering completely. Scatter 1 cup cheese over halibut. Bake, uncovered, for 10 to 12 minutes or until sauce is bubbling around edges and cheese has melted. Dust lightly with paprika or dill.

What's great about this recipe ?

"Easy-Fix"		"Bone Health"	✔
"Quick-Fix"		"Heart Health"	✔
"Easy-Chew"	✔	"Sweetie"	
"Hands-on"		"High Fiber"	

SuperSource: Vits. B2, B3, B6, B12, pant.acid, potassium, magnesium, phosphorus, copper, chromium

Nutrition information per serving: 329 calories, 9 g carbohydrates, 31 g protein, 17 g fat, 7 g saturated fat, 68 mg cholesterol, 447 mg sodium, 1 g fiber. Good source of vits, A, E, B1, iron, calcium, selenium.

Tuna-Zucchini Patties

Servings: 4

These are deceptively simple – and, they're delicious as well! My husband and son love to eat them with ketchup.

1/2 cup chopped onion	1/3 cup chopped parsley
1 tablespoon olive oil	1/8 teaspoon black pepper
1 (6 1/2 ounce) can tuna, drained and flaked	1/4 cup wheat germ
1 cup shredded zucchini	1/2 teaspoon oregano
2 slightly beaten eggs	1/2 teaspoon basil
1/2 cup fine dry bread crumbs	Cooking spray
	1 tablespoon olive oil

1. In small saucepan, cook the onion in olive oil until tender but not brown. Remove from heat. Add tuna, zucchini, eggs, 1/4 cup of the bread crumbs, parsley and pepper. Stir to combine. Shape into six ½" thick patties.
2. In small bowl, stir together remaining bread crumbs, wheat germ, oregano, and basil. Coat tuna patties with this mixture.
3. Spray a medium skillet with cooking spray. Add 1 tablespoon olive oil and heat to medium. Cook patties over medium heat about 3 minutes per side or til golden brown.

What's great about this recipe ?			
"Easy-Fix"	✔	"Bone Health"	✔
"Quick-Fix"	✔	"Heart Health"	✔
"Easy-Chew"	✔	"Sweetie"	
"Hands-on"		"High Fiber"	

SuperSource: Vits. B3, B12, iron, phosphorus

Nutrition information per serving: 278 calories, 16 g carbohydrates, 21 g protein, 14 g fat, 3 g saturated fat, 114 mg cholesterol, 352 mg sodium, 2 g fiber. Good source of vits, B1, B2, E, K, pant.acid, biotin, potassium, selenium, chromium.

Salmon Cakes Garcia

Servings: 4

It's hard to praise this recipe enough–it's rich in protective antioxidants, omega-3 fatty acids, bone-strengthening nutrients, and fiber, too! Do the chopping in a food processor and this dish will go together very quickly.

1 can (14.75 oz) reduced-sodium pink salmon with liquid and bones
1 (8 ounce) can reduced-sodium corn, drained
1 cup dry bread crumbs
1/4 cup wheat germ
1/4 cup ground flax seed
1/2 cup chopped onion
1/2 cup chopped red bell pepper
2 large eggs
4 teaspoons peanut oil
1 lemon, cut in 4 wedges

1. In medium bowl, mash salmon including liquid and bones. Add corn and toss to mix. In small bowl, mix bread crumbs, wheat germ, and flax seed. Add one cup of this mixture to the salmon along with onion, bell pepper, and eggs, and blend well.
2. Spread remaining 1/2 cup crumb mixture on a plate. Shape salmon mixture into 8 oval patties. Coat on both sides with crumbs
3. Heat the oil in non-stick pan. Fry patties in 2 batches, 3 minutes per side til nicely browned, adding more oil if needed. Serve with lemon wedges.

What's great about this recipe ?

"Easy-Fix"	✔	"Bone Health"	✔
"Quick-Fix"	✔	"Heart Health"	✔
"Easy-Chew"	✔	"Sweetie"	
"Hands-on"		"High Fiber"	✔

> **SuperSource: Vits. B1, B2, B3, B6, B12, C, D, E, pant.acid, biotin, potassium, iron, magnesium, phosphorus, copper, manganese, selenium, chromium, fiber**

Nutrition information per serving: 465 calories, 42 g carbohydrates, 33 g protein, 19 g fat, 4 g saturated fat, 165 mg cholesterol, 380 mg sodium, 6 g fiber. Good source of vit. K, folate, calcium, zinc.

Halibut Marengo Style

Servings: 4

A food processor for chopping, plus microwaving, makes this a quick dish to prepare. Reprinted courtesy of the Alaska Seafood Marketing Institute.

4 (4-ounce) halibut steaks
1/4 teaspoon each salt and pepper
2 medium tomatoes, diced
1/2 cup sliced fresh mushrooms
1/2 cup onions, chopped
1/2 cup celery, diced 1/4"

1 tablespoon lemon juice
1 tablespoon peanut oil
1/4 teaspoon thyme, crushed
1/8 teaspoon salt
Dash pepper
1/4 cup chopped parsley

1. Sprinkle halibut with salt and pepper and place in shallow microwave safe dish. Spoon tomato over halibut.
2. In 2 cup microwave safe dish combine mushrooms, onions, celery, lemon juice, oil, thyme, salt and pepper; mix well. Microcook, covered with vented plastic wrap, on high for 2 to 3 minutes or until crisp-tender. Spoon over halibut. Microcook, covered, on high for 4 to 6 minutes or until halibut flakes when tested with a fork. Garnish with chopped parsley.

What's great about this recipe ?

"Easy-Fix"	✔	"Bone Health"	✔
"Quick-Fix"	✔	"Heart Health"	✔
"Easy-Chew"	✔	"Sweetie"	
"Hands-on"		"High Fiber"	

SuperSource: Vits. B3, B6, B12, potassium, magnesium, phosphorus, chromium

Nutrition information per serving: 182 calories, 6 g carbohydrates, 25 g protein, 6 g fat, 1 g saturated fat, 36 mg cholesterol, 302 mg sodium, 2 g fiber. Good source of vits. A, B1, B2, C, E, K, pant.acid, iron, copper.

Mediterranean Fettuccine With Shrimp and Spinach

Servings: 4

One pot cooks the pasta, shrimp, and spinach! To make it easy-chew, chop the shrimp into 1/4" pieces before cooking.* Reprinted courtesy of the National Pasta Association.

12 ounces dry fettuccine, uncooked
1 cup plain non-fat yogurt
1/2 cup crumbled feta cheese
2 cloves garlic, minced
1 tablespoon chopped fresh dill or 1 teaspoon dried dill

1/2 teaspoon freshly ground black pepper
12 ounces medium frozen raw shrimp, thawed
1 10-ounce package frozen chopped spinach, thawed

1. Prepare pasta according to package directions. While the pasta is cooking, stir together the yogurt, feta cheese, garlic, dill and pepper in a large mixing bowl.
2. Two minutes before the pasta is done, stir the shrimp and spinach into the pot with the pasta. Cook two minutes.
3. Drain the pasta, shrimp and spinach thoroughly. Stir into the yogurt mixture and season to taste with salt. Serve immediately.

What's great about this recipe ?

"Easy-Fix"	✔	"Bone Health"	✔
"Quick-Fix"	✔	"Heart Health"	✔
"Easy-Chew"	✔*	"Sweetie"	
"Hands-on"		"High Fiber"	

SuperSource: Vits. A, B1, B2, B3, B6, B12, E, K, folate, iron, calcium, magnesium, phosphorus, zinc, copper, manganese, selenium

Nutrition information per serving: 538 calories, 73 g carbohydrates, 39 g protein, 9 g fat, 5 g saturated fat, 195 mg cholesterol, 656 mg sodium, 4 g fiber. Good source of vit. C, pant.acid, biotin, potassium, chromium, fiber.

Mushroom Pasta Scampi

Servings: 6   Yield: 6 3/4 cups

A great combination of pasta, shrimp, spinach, and mushrooms. Reprinted courtesy of The Mushroom Council.

8 ounces linguini (dry, uncooked)

3 tablespoons olive oil

1 pound fresh white mushrooms, sliced (about 6 cups)

1 tablespoon chopped garlic

1 pound frozen, peeled and deveined uncooked large shrimp, thawed

10 ounces fresh spinach, trimmed and torn into pieces (7 cups)

1/4 teaspoon crushed red pepper

1/4 cup grated Parmesan cheese

1. Cook linguini according to package directions; drain pasta reserving 1/2 cup pasta water; set aside.

2. Meanwhile, heat olive oil in a large skillet. Add mushrooms and garlic; cook and stir until tender and liquid is almost evaporated, about 5 minutes. Add shrimp; cover and cook until shrimp is almost cooked through, about 5 minutes. Stir in spinach and reserved 1/2 cup pasta water; cover and cook until spinach is wilted, about 1 minute. Place pasta in a bowl; stir in mushroom and shrimp mixture, red pepper and Parmesan cheese; toss to combine. Season with salt, if desired.

What's great about this recipe ?

"Easy-Fix"	✔	"Bone Health"	✔
"Quick-Fix"	✔	"Heart Health"	✔
"Easy-Chew"		"Sweetie"	
"Hands-on"		"High Fiber"	

SuperSource: Vits.A, B1, B2, B3, B12, K, folate, pant.acid, potassium, iron, phosphorus, copper, manganese, selenium, chromium

Nutrition information per serving: 328 calories, 35 g carbohydrates, 25 g protein, 10 g fat, 2 g saturated fat, 117 mg cholesterol, 218 mg sodium, 3 g fiber. Good source of vits. C, E, B6, biotin, magnesium, zinc, fiber.

Quick Baked Cod

Servings: 2

This recipe is heart-healthy, high in nutrients, and easy to prepare. Also, if you'd like to lose weight, it's low in calories, yet satisfying. Add a baked sweet potato, some broccoli, and a whole-grain roll. Reprinted courtesy of Alaska Seafood Marketing Institute.

Cooking spray
1/2 pound cod fillets, thawed if frozen
1/4 teaspoon salt
1/4 teaspoon pepper
1 tomato, chopped
1 1/2 teaspoons green onion, chopped

1/4 teaspoon basil, crushed
1/4 teaspoon oregano
1 teaspoon butter or margarine
1/4 cup shredded Monterey jack cheese
1 tablespoon grated Parmesan cheese

1. Preheat oven to 450 degrees F. Spray a small baking dish with cooking spray.
2. Cut cod into serving-size pieces; place in baking dish. Sprinkle with salt and pepper. Combine tomato, green onion, basil, and oregano; spoon over cod. Dot with butter.
3. Bake at 450ºF 8 to 10 minutes or until cod flakes easily when tested with a fork. Sprinkle with cheeses; bake another 5 minutes, or until cheeses melt.

What's great about this recipe ?			
"Easy-Fix"	✔	"Bone Health"	✔
"Quick-Fix"	✔	"Heart Health"	✔
"Easy-Chew"	✔	"Sweetie"	
"Hands-on"		"High Fiber"	

SuperSource: Vit. B12, phosphorus, selenium, chromium

Nutrition information per serving: 186 calories, 3 g carbohydrates, 25 g protein, 8 g fat, 4 g saturated fat, 71 mg cholesterol, 520 mg sodium, 1 g fiber. Good source of vits. A, B1, B3, B6, C, K, potassium, calcium, magnesium .

Snappy Salsa Fillets

Servings: 4

Do the chopping in a food processor, it's easier and quicker.* Good accompaniment: *Garlic Rice with Pine Nuts* or *Lemon Rice* (see *Side Dishes*).

2 cups tomatoes, chopped
1/2 cup onion, chopped about 1/4"
1/2 cup cilantro, minced
1 tablespoon minced fresh jalapeno chile (or less)
1 tablespoon olive oil
2 tablespoons lime juice, preferably freshly squeezed

1 avocado, peeled, seeded, and chopped
1/4 teaspoon salt
1/4 teaspoon black pepper
1 pound fish fillets (red snapper, tilapia, grouper, etc)
1 tablespoon olive oil

1. Stir together tomato, onion, cilantro, jalapeno, oil, lime juice, avocado, salt, and pepper in a large bowl. Marinate for 20 minutes.
2. Preheat broiler. Brush fish fillets with olive oil; sprinkle with salt and pepper. Broil about 4-5 minutes per side (about 10 minutes total per inch of thickness).
3. Serve with salsa.

What's great about this recipe ?

"Easy-Fix"	✔*	"Bone Health"	✔
"Quick-Fix"	✔*	"Heart Health"	✔
"Easy-Chew"		"Sweetie"	
"Hands-on"		"High Fiber"	

SuperSource: Vits. B6, B12, C, pant.acid, potassium, phosphorus, copper, selenium

Nutrition information per serving: 280 calories, 10 g carbohydrates, 25 g protein, 16 g fat, 2 g saturated fat, 42 mg cholesterol, 265 mg sodium, 4 g fiber. Good source of vits. A, B1, B3, E, K, folate, iron, magnesium, manganese, chromium, fiber.

Nutty Chicken Salad

Servings: 4

This salad is substantial enough for a light main dish. It's full of heart-protective nuts and seeds, which also increase the fiber. Serve with whole-grain bread or rolls and a piece of fruit.

Dressing:
1/4 cup sugar
1/4 teaspoon paprika
1/2 teaspoon dry mustard
1/4 teaspoon salt
1/4 cup white wine vinegar
1/4 cup sunflower oil
2 teaspoons poppy seeds

1 (10 ounce) can chunk white chicken, drained and broken into chunks
1/2 cup celery, diced 1/4"
3 green onions with 2" of green tops, sliced
1/4 cup sesame seeds, toasted
1/3 cup walnut halves, toasted
2 cups Romaine lettuce, chopped

1. In small bowl, whisk together sugar, paprika, mustard, salt, wine vinegar, oil, and poppy seeds. Set aside.
2. In large bowl, mix together chicken, celery, and green onions. Pour dressing over chicken mixture and toss gently to mix. Refrigerate until chilled, about 2 hours. At serving time, mix chicken mixture with sesame seeds, walnuts, and lettuce.

What's great about this recipe ?

"Easy-Fix"	✔	"Bone Health"	✔
"Quick-Fix"		"Heart Health"	✔
"Easy-Chew"		"Sweetie"	
"Hands-on"		"High Fiber"	

SuperSource: Vits. E, K, iron, copper, manganese

Nutrition information per serving: 390 calories, 20 g carbohydrates, 20 g protein, 28 g fat, 5 g saturated fat, 35 mg cholesterol, 364 mg sodium, 3 g fiber. Good source of vits. B1, folate, biotin, magnesium, phosphorus, zinc, chromium, fiber.

Crockery Turkey Wing Dinner

Servings: 2

Turkey wings are often overlooked, yet they're inexpensive and easy to cook in a crockery cooker. To make it easy-chew, remove meat from bones and chop; mash vegetables.* This recipe technically isn't quick, but the preparation time is short, and it's nice to know your evening meal will be ready when you are.

1 turkey wing	1 medium onion, peeled
2 medium potatoes with skin (10 ounces), scrubbed	2 parsnips, scrubbed
	1/4 teaspoon salt
2 large carrots, scrubbed	1/4 teaspoon pepper

1. Rinse turkey wing. Cut potatoes and onion into quarters, carrot and parsnip into 1" chunks.
2. Place a steamer or other small rack on floor of crockery cooker (at least a 3 1/2-quart size). It should rise about ½" above the bottom of the cooker. Place wing and vegetables on rack; sprinkle with salt and pepper. Cover cooker and turn on. Cook on low about 8 hours. The turkey will cook sooner than the vegetables, but the steam inside the cooker will keep it moist. The fat from the turkey will drain off, leaving a low-fat meal.
3. Pile wing and vegetables onto a platter and serve at once.

What's great about this recipe ?

"Easy-Fix"	✔	"Bone Health"	✔
"Quick-Fix"		"Heart Health"	✔
"Easy-Chew"	✔*	"Sweetie"	
"Hands-on"		"High Fiber"	✔

SuperSource: Vits. A, B1, B3, B6, C, pant.acid, potassium, iron, phosphorus, zinc, copper, manganese, selenium, chromium, fiber

Nutrition information per serving: 478 calories, 62 g carbohydrates, 31 g protein, 12 g fat, 3 g saturated fat, 76 mg cholesterol, 392 mg sodium, 9 g fiber. Good source of vits. B2, B12, K, folate, biotin, magnesium.

Chicken, Peas, and Mushrooms in Sour Cream Sauce

Servings 2

A delicious, and easy-to-chew way to serve chicken. Try with a dish of sliced tomatoes drizzled with olive oil, salt, pepper, and basil.

2 teaspoons olive oil
2 (3 ounce) boneless, skinless chicken breasts, cut in 1/2" to 1/4" dice
1/4 teaspoon black pepper
1/2 cup dairy sour cream
1/2 teaspoon reduced-sodium soy sauce

1/2 teaspoon paprika
1 tablespoon dry white wine or water
1 1/2 cups frozen peas, thawed
1 (4 ounce) can mushrooms, drained
1 tablespoon grated Parmesan cheese
2 slices whole-wheat bread, toasted and cut into triangles

1. Heat 10-inch skillet over medium heat, add olive oil, and heat at medium temperature, about 2 minutes. Add diced chicken in one layer; cook about 4 minutes. Turn all pieces and cook until light brown, about 4 minutes more. Sprinkle with pepper.
2. Whisk together sour cream, soy sauce, and paprika, and stir into skillet, mixing well. Reduce temperature to low and cook until heated through, about 4 minutes. Stir in white wine and cook 1 minute more.
3. Meanwhile thaw peas under hot running water til thawed and warmed through. Stir peas and mushrooms into skillet and pour all into greased 1-1/2 quart shallow baking dish. Sprinkle with Parmesan cheese and broil in oven until light brown, about 4 minutes. Serve on toast points.

What's great about this recipe ?			
"Easy-Fix"	✔	"Bone Health"	✔
"Quick-Fix"	✔	"Heart Health"	
"Easy-Chew"	✔	"Sweetie"	
"Hands-on"		"High Fiber"	✔

SuperSource: Vits.B1, B2, B3, B6, K, pant.acid, iron, phosphorus, zinc, copper, manganese, chromium, fiber

Nutrition information per serving: 432 calories, 35 g carbohydrates, 32 g protein, 18 g fat, 8 g saturated fat, 73 mg cholesterol, 672 mg sodium, 10 g fiber. Good source of vits. A, E, B12, C, folate, potassium, calcium, magnesium.

Southwest Chicken-Pasta Casserole

Servings: 6

Buying pre-cooked chicken breasts makes this recipe faster, but you can easily bake your own. Leave out the jalapeno if you don't like the heat. To make it easier to chew, dice the chicken into 1/2" pieces.* Reprinted courtesy of the National Pasta Association.

1 pound rigatoni, ziti or other medium pasta shape, uncooked
2 teaspoons peanut oil
1 medium onion, chopped
1 garlic clove, minced
1 jalapeño, seeded and minced
3 tablespoons chili powder
1 28-ounce can diced tomatoes, undrained

1 teaspoon cumin
1 teaspoon dried oregano
3 tablespoons ground flax seed
8 ounces cooked boneless, skinless chicken breast, julienned
1/4 cup ripe olives
1 cup grated Monterey Jack cheese (4 oz.), divided

1. Preheat oven to 375°F. Prepare pasta according to package directions; drain.
2. While pasta is cooking, heat the oil in a medium saucepan over medium heat. Add the onion, garlic and jalapeño and cook until softened, about 3 minutes. Add the chili powder and stir for 1 minute. Add the tomatoes and liquid, cumin, and oregano. Simmer until slightly thickened, about 15 minutes.
3. In a bowl, combine pasta, flax seed, chicken, olives, 3/4 cup of cheese, and sauce. Spoon into a 2-quart baking dish sprayed with cooking spray.
4. Sprinkle the reserved cheese on top. Cover loosely with foil and bake until warmed through and the cheese melts, about 15 minutes.

What's great about this recipe ?			
"Easy-Fix"		"Bone Health"	✔
"Quick-Fix"		"Heart Health"	
"Easy-Chew"	✔*	"Sweetie"	
"Hands-on"		"High Fiber"	

SuperSource: Vits. A, B1, B2, B3, iron

Nutrition information per serving: 515 calories, 64 g carbohydrates, 27 g protein, 15 g fat, 5 g saturated fat, 127 mg cholesterol, 549 mg sodium, 5 g fiber. Good source of vits. B6, B12, C, calcium, phosphorus, selenium, chromium, fiber.

Chicken with Rice and Mushrooms

Servings: 2

To make it easier to chew, dice the chicken before putting it on top of rice.* Pickled beets or a shredded carrot salad would go well with this dish.

2 cups reduced-sodium chicken broth or 2 cups water plus 1 chicken bouillon cube

1 cup long-grain brown rice, such as Basmati or Texmati, rinsed and drained

1 (4 ounce) can peas, drained

2 boneless, skinless chicken breast halves

4 tablespoons lime juice

2 tablespoons olive oil

1/2 teaspoon salt

1/2 teaspoon black pepper

1 (4 ounce) can sliced mushrooms

1. In medium saucepan, bring chicken broth and rice to boil. Cover, reduce heat, and simmer, about 25-35 minutes, till tender. Remove from heat; stir in drained peas and keep covered till ready to serve.

2. Meantime, preheat broiler, setting broiler rack about 6 inches from heat. In small bowl, mix lime juice and olive oil. Dip chicken breasts in mixture, covering completely. Line small baking pan with foil, lay chicken breasts side by side. Sprinkle with salt and pepper.

3. Broil chicken about 10-15 minutes, till golden brown; turn and pour remaining lime-oil mixture over chicken. Continue to broil about 10-15 minutes more or until fork can be inserted in chicken with ease. Pour mushrooms over chicken and return to oven for about 2 minutes or until mushrooms are hot.

4. Remove rice to serving dish. Place chicken on top of rice. Pour over chicken any juices remaining in baking pan.

What's great about this recipe ?

"Easy-Fix"	✔	"Bone Health"	✔
"Quick-Fix"	✔	"Heart Health"	✔
"Easy-Chew"	✔*	"Sweetie"	
"Hands-on"		"High Fiber"	

SuperSource: Vits. B3, B6, pant.acid, iron, phosphorus, copper

Nutrition information per serving: 628 calories, 74 g carbohydrates, 38 g protein, 10 g fat, 3 g saturated fat, 69 mg cholesterol, 470 mg sodium, 5 g fiber. Good source of vits. B1, B2, B12, E, potassium, magnesium, zinc, fiber.

Chicken a la Can

Servings: 2
Super-easy version of Chicken a la King; the recipe is easily doubled.

2 teaspoons olive oil
1 ounce mushrooms, chopped 1/4"
    (about 2-3 mushrooms) or 1/4
    cup canned mushrooms
1/3 cup diced green bell pepper
1 tablespoon onion, diced 1/4"
2 teaspoons butter
1 tablespoon flour
1/8 teaspoon salt
1/8 teaspoon black pepper

1/3 cup chicken broth
1/3 cup evaporated skim milk
1 egg yolk, lightly beaten
1 teaspoon lemon juice
1 teaspoon sherry, optional
1 (5 ounce) can chicken, drained and
    diced
2 cups cooked brown rice
2 teaspoons pimiento, diced

1. In 10" skillet, over medium heat, cook mushrooms, bell pepper and onion in oil till tender, about 5-8 minutes; remove and set aside. Melt butter in same pan; add flour, salt, and pepper. Cook, stirring, for 1 minute without browning.
2. In small bowl, combine broth and skim milk. Gradually stir mixture into skillet. Bring to a boil and cook, stirring, until sauce is smooth and thickened, about 3 to 5 minutes.
3. Gradually whisk 1/4 cup sauce into the egg yolk. Stir back into pan until well blended. Add vegetables, lemon juice, sherry, and chicken. Cook until heated through, about 5 minutes. Serve over hot rice, garnished with pimiento.

What's great about this recipe ?			
"Easy-Fix"	✔	"Bone Health"	✔
"Quick-Fix"	✔	"Heart Health"	✔
"Easy-Chew"	✔	"Sweetie"	
"Hands-on"		"High Fiber"	

SuperSource: Vits.B1, B2, B3, B6, C, pant.acid, iron, magnesium, phosphorus, copper, manganese, selenium

Nutrition information per serving: 479 calories, 58 g carbohydrates, 27 g protein, 16 g fat, 5 g saturated fat, 154 mg cholesterol, 570 mg sodium, 5 g fiber. Good source of vits. A, B12, K, biotin, potassium, calcium, zinc, chromium, fiber.

Chicken a la Crock

Serves: 2

Somewhere between chicken stew and roasted chicken. A one-pot meal that doesn't have to be tended. Serve with whole-grain bread or rolls, applesauce dusted with cinnamon, a glass of white wine or fruit juice.

1 large potato, sliced 1/4" (about 10 ounces)

1 onion sliced 1/4"

2 carrots, sliced diagonally 1/4"

1 celery stalk, sliced 1/4"

2 skinless, boneless chicken breast halves (about 8 ounces total), thawed if frozen

1/4 cup chicken broth, or 1/4 cup water plus 1/2 chicken bouillon cube

1/4 teaspoon black pepper

1/4 teaspoon garlic powder

1. Layer potato slices in crockery cooker (at least 2 quart size). Layer over them the onion, then carrot, then celery. Lay chicken breasts on top of vegetables.
2. In small bowl, mix chicken broth (or water plus dissolved bouillon cube), pepper, and garlic powder. Pour mixture over chicken and vegetables. Cover pot; cook on Low for about 8 hours. Dice chicken and vegetables 1/4" before serving, if needed for easy chewing.*

What's great about this recipe ?			
"Easy-Fix"	✔	"Bone Health"	✔
"Quick-Fix"		"Heart Health"	✔
"Easy-Chew"	✔*	"Sweetie"	
"Hands-on"		"High Fiber"	✔

SuperSource: Vits.A, B1, B3, B6, C, pant.acid, potassium, iron, phosphorus, copper, manganese, chromium, fiber

Nutrition information per serving: 353 calories, 51 g carbohydrates, 33 g protein, 2 g fat, 1 g saturated fat, 69 mg cholesterol, 258 mg sodium, 7 g fiber. Good source of vits. B2, B12, K, folate, biotin, magnesium, zinc.

Ginger Chicken Rice Bowls

Servings: 4

You can substitute a 10-ounce can of chunk chicken, if you prefer. A bonus: you can freeze individual servings for an even quicker meal later! Recipe © USA Rice Federation.

1/4 cup reduced sodium teriyaki sauce
1/4 cup plus 1 tablespoon water
8 ounces boneless, skinless chicken breasts, cut into 1/2-inch pieces
2 tablespoons peanut oil
1 medium onion, cut into eight wedges

1 (16-ounce) package frozen broccoli, cauliflower and carrot mixture
1/2 teaspoon ground ginger
1/3 cup dry white wine, chicken broth, or water
1 tablespoon cornstarch
3 cups hot cooked brown rice

1. In shallow baking dish, combine teriyaki sauce with 1/4 cup water; add chicken, coating well. Cover and refrigerate two hours. Drain marinade from chicken and discard.
2. Lightly brown chicken and onion in oil in large skillet over medium-high heat. Stir in frozen vegetables, ginger and wine. Cover; simmer 4 to 5 minutes, or until vegetables are tender-crisp.
3. Stir cornstarch with 1 tablespoon water until smooth. Slowly add to skillet, stirring occasionally, until thickened. Divide hot cooked rice equally into four individual bowls. Spoon chicken mixture over rice.
4. Note: Individual rice bowls may be stored in the freezer for up to one month. To reheat frozen rice bowls, microwave on HIGH 5 to 7 minutes, or until heated through. Let stand in microwave 1 to 2 minutes.

What's great about this recipe ?

"Easy-Fix"	✔	"Bone Health"	✔
"Quick-Fix"	✔	"Heart Health"	✔
"Easy-Chew"	✔	"Sweetie"	
"Hands-on"		"High Fiber"	

SuperSource: Vits. B3, B6, C, phosphorus, manganese, selenium

Nutrition information per serving: 374 calories, 49 g carbohydrates, 20 g protein, 9 g fat, 2 g saturated fat, 33 mg cholesterol, 291 mg sodium, 6 g fiber. Good source of vits. B1, pant.acid, potassium, iron, magnesium, zinc, copper, chromium, fiber.

Burgers Dijon

Servings: 6

The flax seed and wheat germ add fiber and valuable protective fats to these juicy burgers. Good accompaniments: Whole-grain bread, butter, coleslaw and a baked potato, with a glass of grape juice.

3 tablespoons Dijon mustard
2 tablespoons honey
1/2 teaspoon dried oregano
1 pound lean ground beef
1 teaspoon dried parsley

1 teaspoon dried oregano
1/4 cup diced onion
1/4 teaspoon black pepper
3 tablespoons ground flax seed
3 tablespoons wheat germ

1. Combine mustard, honey and 1/2 teaspoon oregano; set aside.
2. Combine ground beef, 2 tablespoons honey-mustard sauce, parsley, remaining teaspoon oregano, onion, pepper, flax seed, and wheat germ, blending well. Divide mixture into 6 portions; shape into 1/2" thick patties.

3. Heat large heavy nonstick skillet over medium for 5 minutes. Cook patties about 4 minutes per side. Place burgers on paper towels to drain off excess fat. Place on plates, spooning remaining sauce over.

What's great about this recipe ?			
"Easy-Fix"	✔	"Bone Health"	✔
"Quick-Fix"	✔	"Heart Health"	✔
"Easy-Chew"	✔	"Sweetie"	
"Hands-on"		"High Fiber"	

SuperSource: Vit.B12, iron, zinc, selenium

Nutrition information per serving: 252 calories, 9 g carbohydrates, 18 g protein, 16 g fat, 6 g saturated fat, 59 mg cholesterol, 100 mg sodium, 2 g fiber. Good source of vits. B2, B3, B6, potassium, magnesium, phosphorus, copper, manganese.

Steak Salad with Asian Dressing

Servings: 4

A fresh, savory way to eat your beef – and it's not hard on the arteries, either! Most of the fat is the heart-healthy kind. Use your food processor for shredding and slicing. If chewing is difficult, you can shred all of the vegetables, and cut the beef into smaller pieces.*

Marinade/Dressing:
1/2 cup rice vinegar
2 tablespoons Asian sesame oil
3 tablespoons low sodium soy sauce
1/4 cup water
2 tablespoons sliced green onions
2-3 teaspoons sugar (to taste)
1 tablespoon minced fresh ginger (or bottled minced ginger, or 1 tsp dried ground ginger)

4 tablespoons sesame seeds
12 ounces boneless top sirloin steak, fat trimmed, cut into 1-inch-wide slices
4 cups Chinese (napa) cabbage, shredded
1 cup shredded carrots
1/2 cup sliced radishes
1 cup sliced cucumber
2 cups cooked brown rice

1. Whisk together vinegar, oil, soy sauce, water, green onions, sugar, and ginger; set aside. Toast sesame seeds in medium-hot skillet 2 minutes, or till fragrant; set aside.
2. Place steak in nonreactive glass or plastic bowl; add 1/3 cup marinade, stirring to coat. Marinate in refrigerator 2 hours, stirring to coat every 30 minutes. Remove steak and discard marinade.
3. Place steak on rack in broiler pan about 3 to 4 inches from heat. Broil 16 to 21 minutes for rare to medium, turning once. Let stand 5 minutes. Slice thinly.
4. While steak is broiling, combine cabbage, carrots, radishes, and cucumbers and divide equally among 4 plates. Place a serving of brown rice in the center. Divide steak slices among the plates, arranging on top of salad.
5. Pour remaining dressing over salad, beef, and rice. Sprinkle sesame seeds over all.

What's great about this recipe ?

"Easy-Fix"	✔	"Bone Health"	✔
"Quick-Fix"		"Heart Health"	✔
"Easy-Chew"	✔*	"Sweetie"	
"Hands-on"		"High Fiber"	

SuperSource: Vits. A, B1, B2, B3, B6, B12, C, K, potassium, iron, phosphorus, zinc, copper, manganese, selenium

Nutrition information per serving: 446 calories, 32 g carbohydrates, 33 g protein, 19 g fat, 4 g saturated fat, 76 mg cholesterol, 557 mg sodium, 5 g fiber. Good source of folate, pant. acid, magnesium, fiber.

Pat Garcia's Meatballs Two Ways

Servings: 8   One serving: 2 meatballs

These can be frozen for handy snacks later, or eaten at once. They can be eaten from a cocktail pick if you like; but if you love spaghetti and meatballs, just boil up the spaghetti!

1 (28 ounce) jar low-sodium spaghetti sauce, divided (set aside 1/2 cup)
1 egg
3/4 cup seasoned bread crumbs
1/4 cup ground flax seed
1 medium onion, chopped

1/2 cup chopped sweet red pepper
1 garlic clove, minced
1/2 teaspoon Italian seasoning
1/4 teaspoon pepper
1 pound ground beef
1 pound spaghetti (optional)
1 ounce grated Parmesan cheese

1. In bowl, combine 1/2 cup spaghetti sauce, egg, bread crumbs, flax, onion, red pepper, garlic, Italian seasoning and pepper. Add ground beef and mix together, blending well. Shape into 16 one-inch balls. Place balls in a single layer on ungreased 15"x10"x1" baking pan. Bake at 350 deg. F. 20-30 minutes or til meat is no longer pink in center, turning once. Set meatballs on paper towels to drain off fat.
2. *To serve as a snack:* Insert cocktail picks. Eat meatballs plain or dipped in remaining spaghetti sauce. Extras can be frozen for snacks later.
3. *To serve with spaghetti:* Transfer meatballs to saucepan; add remaining spaghetti sauce. Bring to boil; reduce heat, cover and simmer 15 minutes. Boil spaghetti according to package directions. Drain; place in serving bowl. Add meatballs and sauce, and toss lightly to combine. Serve with Parmesan cheese, if desired.

What's great about this recipe ?			
"Easy-Fix"		"Bone Health"	✔
"Quick-Fix"	✔	"Heart Health"	✔
"Easy-Chew"	✔	"Sweetie"	
"Hands-on"	✔	"High Fiber"	

SuperSource: Vit.B12, iron, zinc, selenium

Nutrition information per serving (without spaghetti): 252 calories, 13 g carbohydrates, 18 g protein, 14 g fat, 5 g saturated fat, 76 mg cholesterol, 366 mg sodium, 2 g fiber. Good source of vitamins B2, B3, B6, C, potassium, magnesium, phosphorus, copper, chromium.

Beefy Quesadillas

Servings: 4

These are quick, easy to prepare, and satisfying. To make them easier to chew, cut the roast beef into 1/4-1/2" dice.* Add a glass of low-sodium tomato juice, and a bowl of fruit salad. Reprinted courtesy of the National Cattlemen's Beef Association.

1 small onion, chopped
1/2 cup diced red bell pepper
1/2 cup prepared medium salsa, divided

3/4 cup shredded Cheddar or Monterey Jack cheese
4 (8") whole-wheat flour tortillas
6 ounces purchased thin-sliced roast beef

1. Place onion and bell pepper in small microwave-safe bowl. Cover and microwave at HIGH 3 to 4 minutes, stirring halfway through cooking time. Stir in 3 tablespoons salsa; reserve.
2. Sprinkle equal amount of cheese evenly on each tortilla. Arrange deli roast beef over cheese; top with equal amount of reserved vegetable mixture. Fold tortillas over to close.
3. Meanwhile heat 10-inch nonstick skillet over medium heat 5 minutes. Cook two quesadillas in skillet 2 to 2 1/2 minutes, turning once. Repeat with remaining quesadillas. Serve with remaining salsa.
4. Microwave Directions: Place two quesadillas on 12-inch microwave-safe plate. Cover with moistened paper towel. Microwave at HIGH 1 to 1 1/2 minutes or until hot. Repeat with remaining 2 quesadillas.

What's great about this recipe ?			
"Easy-Fix"	✔	"Bone Health"	✔
"Quick-Fix"	✔	"Heart Health"	✔
"Easy-Chew"	✔*	"Sweetie"	
"Hands-on"	✔	"High Fiber"	✔

SuperSource: Vit.B12, iron, phosphorus, selenium, chromium, fiber

Nutrition information per serving: 237 calories, 15 g carbohydrates, 22 g protein, 10 g fat, 6 g saturated fat, 55 mg cholesterol, 580 mg sodium, 10 g fiber. Good source of vits. B1, B2, B3, B6, C, calcium, zinc.

Microwaved Pasta with Ham and Mushrooms

Servings: 6

Microwaving speeds up preparation; you can also purchase ready-sliced mushrooms and ready-cooked ham.* For easier chewing, cut ham and zucchini in 1/2" pieces. Reprinted courtesy of The Mushroom Council.

16 ounces rotelle (corkscrew) pasta
1 tablespoon minced garlic
2 tablespoons butter
1 pound fresh mushrooms, sliced
1 (13 3/4-ounce) can reduced-sodium chicken broth
2 tablespoons cornstarch

1 tablespoon ground flax seed
1/4 teaspoon ground black pepper
2 cups zucchini, cut 1 × 1/4"
6 ounces cooked ham, cut in 1-1/2" ×1/2" strips (about 1-1/2 cups)
1 cup cherry tomato halves
1/4 cup grated Parmesan cheese

1. Cook pasta according to manufacturer's directions; drain and put in a large serving bowl.
2. Meanwhile, in a 12 × 8 × 2-inch microwaveable baking pan, place garlic and butter. Microwave on HIGH (100% power) until garlic is softened, about 2 minutes. Stir in mushrooms; microwave uncovered on HIGH until mushrooms are nearly tender, about 8 minutes, stirring once.
3. In a cup stir broth, cornstarch, salt and pepper until smooth; stir into mushrooms. Microwave uncovered on HIGH until hot, about 8 minutes, stirring once. Add zucchini, ham and cherry tomatoes; microwave uncovered on HIGH until mixture thickens and boils, about 9 minutes, stirring twice. Stir in Parmesan cheese; pour over reserved pasta; toss gently. Serve with additional Parmesan cheese if desired.

What's great about this recipe ?			
"Easy-Fix"	✔	"Bone Health"	✔
"Quick-Fix"	✔*	"Heart Health"	✔
"Easy-Chew"	✔	"Sweetie"	
"Hands-on"		"High Fiber"	

SuperSource: Vits.B1,B2,B3,pant.acid, iron, phosphorus, copper, chromium

Nutrition information per serving: 421 calories, 68 g carbohydrates, 20 g protein, 8 g fat, 4 g saturated fat, 28 mg cholesterol, 472 mg sodium, 4 g fiber. Good source of vits. B6, C, folate, potassium, magnesium, zinc, selenium, fiber.

Saucy Ground Beef

Servings: 4

Serve this "comfort food" with baked sweet potato and green beans.

1 pound lean ground beef
1 cup chopped onion
1 small clove garlic, minced, or ½ teaspoon garlic powder
1 (4.5 ounce) can mushrooms, drained
1/4 teaspoon ground black pepper
1 cup hot water

3 beef bouillon cubes
2 tablespoons tomato paste
3/4 cup cold water
2 tablespoons whole-wheat flour
3 tablespoons ground flax seed
8 ounces egg noodles, cooked and drained
1 tablespoon olive oil

1. In large skillet, over medium heat, cook crumbled beef till browned. Drain off fat. Add onions and garlic; cook till onion is lightly browned. Add mushrooms, and pepper to taste.
2. Dissolve bouillon cubes in 1 cup hot water; stir in tomato paste. Add to browned meat.
3. Stir flour into 3/4 cup cold water, whisking till smooth; whisk in flax seed. Stir into meat mixture. Lower heat to simmer, and cook about one hour, till thickened.
4. Toss cooked noodles with olive oil. Transfer to serving bowl. Spoon meat mixture over noodles. Serve immediately.

What's great about this recipe ?

"Easy-Fix"	✔	"Bone Health"	✔
"Quick-Fix"		"Heart Health"	✔
"Easy-Chew"	✔	"Sweetie"	
"Hands-on"		"High Fiber"	

SuperSource: Vits. B1, B2, B3, B6, B12, iron, phosphorus, zinc, copper, manganese, selenium, chromium

Nutrition information per serving: 568 calories, 53 g carbohydrates, 32 g protein, 17 g fat, 5 g saturated fat, 125 mg cholesterol, 764 mg sodium, 5 g fiber. Good source of folate, pant.acid, potassium, magnesium, fiber.

Updated Shepherd's Pie

Servings: 4

To save time, microwave the potatoes; then mash (include the skins for extra fiber) with the egg and water. If you boil the potatoes, use some of the cooking water to mash them. You can use either fresh or canned tomatoes.

12 ounces lean ground beef
1 teaspoon dried basil
1 onion, chopped
1 clove garlic, minced; or 1/4 tsp garlic powder
1 (15 ounce) can green beans, drained
1 cup diced tomatoes

2 unpeeled baking potatoes, baked, diced and mashed
1 egg, beaten
1/2 cup water
1/4 cup ground flax seed
1/4 cup shredded Cheddar or Monterey Jack cheese (optional)

1. Preheat oven to 350 degrees F. Heat a large skillet over medium heat. Crumble beef into skillet, add basil, and cook till beef is browned, about 5 minutes. Pour off fat. Add onion and saute till lightly browned, 4- 5 minutes. Stir in garlic, green beans and tomatoes; lower heat, and simmer 5 minutes. Spoon cooked mixture into 2 quart baking dish.
2. In medium bowl, mix potato with beaten egg, water, and flax seed. Spread over browned beef mixture in baking dish.
3. Bake at 350 degrees F. 15 to 20 minutes, or until potatoes are golden brown. Sprinkle with cheese, bake about 5 minutes more or till cheese is melted.

What's great about this recipe ?

"Easy-Fix"	✔	"Bone Health"	✔
"Quick-Fix"		"Heart Health"	✔
"Easy-Chew"	✔	"Sweetie"	
"Hands-on"		"High Fiber"	✔

SuperSource: Vits. B2, B3, B6, B12, C, potassium, iron, phosphorus, zinc, copper, manganese, selenium, chromium, fiber

Nutrition information per serving: 445 calories, 39 g carbohydrates, 26 g protein, 21 g fat, 8 g saturated fat, 120 mg cholesterol, 436 mg sodium, 7 g fiber. Good source of vits. A, B1, K, folate, pant. acid, biotin, magnesium.

SIDE DISHES
Grains, Vegetables, Fruits

Green, orange, red, yellow, blue, purple, and gold – vegetables and fruits come in a rainbow of colors, and provide a wealth of vitamins, minerals, and phytochemicals, sugars, complex carbohydrates, and fibers. Grains aren't as colorful, but they have the starch we need for energy, as well as trace minerals and even more fibers.

It's a good idea to have a mixture of both cooked and raw vegetables and fruits – some don't give up their nutrient treasures until cooked, while in other cases, cooking destroys some important vitamins. So try to eat some of your vegetables and fruits both ways whenever possible.

Grains are best eaten entire, rather than polished, degerminated, or stripped of their bran. Whole wheat, for example, contains precious vitamin E, trace minerals, and protective insoluble fiber, and can be ground into flour, cracked, or cooked whole. Oats are a fine source of soluble fiber and can help lower cholesterol; oats are most often rolled and eaten as a cooked cereal at breakfast. Grains in their whole, uncut state, usually take a lot of cooking, so make a large pot, then measure out into one-cup portions, and freeze – it will make many recipes quick and easy to prepare. Here, I also offer recipes for quinoa, because, besides a high nutrient content, it also cooks much faster than many other grains.

If chewing becomes a problem, then the raw or cooked grain can be chopped or ground in a food processor or blender. Raw brown rice can be coarsely ground in this way, then cooked into a delicious, quick-cooking breakfast cereal. Cooked rice can also be ground, to make it easier to chew. Other excellent grains include barley, dried corn (not a true grain, but similar in many ways), and the quick-cooking quinoa.

Grains

Whole grains are a vital source of minerals and fibers, and it's important to include them daily. A drawback is that some, such as rice and barley, take a long time to cook. But that doesn't mean they can't be a "convenience food" – just cook a big pot of rice, and freeze it in one-cup portions, in a zip-top bag. Flatten the bag as much as possible, stack the bags on top of one another, and freeze. Then, when you need it, the flattened bag thaws quickly, ready to heat up as is or pop into a casserole.

There are many kinds of rice, but only three used in this book – short and medium grain; long grain; and basmati or Texmati which is a small, very thin grain with an aromatic, nutty flavor. The short and medium grains take longer to cook, usually from 45 to 60 minutes; long-grain rice may cook in 35-40 minutes; while basmati and Texmati cook the quickest, in about 25 - 35 minutes. Time may also vary depending on the humidity or dryness of your storage conditions, and the altitude – water boils at a lower temperature at higher altitudes, and rice will take longer to cook.

Short and medium grain rice types have the richest flavor; after cooking, the grains expand and become sticky, clinging together. This is a good rice for soups, casseroles, rice pudding, and risotto. Long-grain brown rice grains stay separate and fluffy when cooked, making them a good choice for pilafs and stir-fries. Basmati and Texmati cook the quickest, and are delicious as is, with a pat of butter, or in pilafs. To cook brown rice in a pressure cooker, shorten time to 20-22 minutes for all types.

> For variety, you may want to substitute chicken or beef broth for the water; or add a bouillon cube at the start of cooking. If you do, be sure to label the rice "flavored" before freezing – you wouldn't want to make rice pudding later on, and find out it was chicken-flavored! You may also add turmeric, for a beautiful yellow color, to dress up your meal. *(See Getting Started - Turmeric.)*

In general, rice should be cooked covered without stirring (paellas and risottos are exceptions). A glass heat-proof pot works very well, because you can see when the rice comes to a boil, and also check to see if it becomes too dry or scorches.

Here are some basic cooking directions to get you started using these valuable grains.

Brown Rice

Servings: 6   Yield: 3 cups

If you wish, substitute chicken, beef, or vegetable broth for the water, or add a bouillon cube at the start of cooking. You may also add 1/2 teaspoon of turmeric, for its lovely yellow color, and possible health benefits.

1 cup brown rice, rinsed   ½ teaspoon salt
2 cups water

1. Place rice, water, and salt in a 2-quart saucepan with a tight-fitting lid. Bring to a boil, then reduce heat to a simmer and cook:
   - short / medium grain about 50 - 60 minutes
   - long grain about 35 - 45 minutes
   - Texmati / basmati about 25 - 35 minutes

   Rice should be tender, and rice on the bottom of the pan should be golden brown, but not scorched.
2. Remove from heat and allow to sit, covered, for another 5-10 minutes. Fluff with a fork to separate grains. May be eaten plain or with a pat of butter; or covered with sauce or gravy.
3. To freeze: Cool rice. Measure out one-cup portions, place in zip-lock plastic bags. Flatten bags, stack them on top of one another, and freeze.
4. To use: remove as many portions as you need; thaw under cool running water, or remove from bag, place in microwave-safe covered dish, and microwave at "defrost" or medium for 2-3 minutes, until thawed.

What's great about this recipe ?

"Easy-Fix"	✔	"Bone Health"	✔
"Quick-Fix"		"Heart Health"	✔
"Easy-Chew"	✔	"Sweetie"	
"Hands-on"		"High Fiber"	

SuperSource: Manganese

Nutrition information per serving: 115 calories, 24 g carbohydrates, 2 g protein, 1 g fat, 0 g saturated fat, 0 mg cholesterol, 195 mg sodium, 1 g fiber. Good source of vits. B1, magnesium, phosphorus, selenium.

Barley

Servings: 4

Barley is an ancient grain, though not as widely used today. Nevertheless, it's a valuable food. Look for "hulled barley" or "barley groats." Only the tough outer hulls are polished off, the wonderful bran and germ, with their many minerals and vitamins, are still present. "Pearl barley" is much quicker-cooking, but the vital nutrients and bran are lost.

Whole hulled barley must be soaked overnight, so make a double batch and freeze plenty. Drain off the soaking water, then add more water and cook about one hour. If chewing is a problem, you can put the cooked barley in a food processor and coarsely chop it.*

1 cup hulled barley	1/4 teaspoon salt
3 cups water	

1. Rinse the barley well and place it in a large pot. Cover with 2 inches of water and let soak overnight.
2. In the morning, drain off the soaking water and add 3 cups water and the salt. Bring to a boil, cover tightly, lower heat to simmer, and cook about 60 minutes, checking occasionally to see if it needs extra water.
3. Cool barley, and measure out one-cup portions. Place in zip-top plastic freezer bags. Flatten bags, and stack them in the freezer.
4. When barley is needed for a recipe, take out the required amount and run lukewarm water over the freezer bags to thaw.

What's great about this recipe ?			
"Easy-Fix"	✔	"Bone Health"	✔
"Quick-Fix"		"Heart Health"	✔
"Easy-Chew"	✔*	"Sweetie"	
"Hands-on"		"High Fiber"	✔

> **SuperSource: Copper, manganese, selenium, fiber**

Nutrition information per serving: 163 calories, 34 g carbohydrates, 6 g protein, 1 g fat, 0 g saturated fat, 0 mg cholesterol, 151 mg sodium, 8 g fiber. Good source of vits. B1, B2, B3, iron, magnesium, phosphorus, zinc.

Cashew Rice

Servings: 6

Use your precooked frozen rice for faster preparation; just heat it in the microwave or in a covered skillet over low heat. You can also get bottled minced ginger and garlic, to save time and effort.

1/2 cup cashews	1/4 cup green onions
1 tablespoon olive oil	1 tablespoon minced garlic
1 teaspoon fresh ginger, grated	3 cups hot cooked rice

1. Heat large skillet over medium-low heat. Add cashews and toast lightly, just till golden brown. Remove and set aside.
2. Add oil to skillet and raise heat to medium. Saute ginger, onions, and garlic about 2 minutes or till garlic is golden. Add rice and stir-fry till well mixed and heated through. Spoon into serving dish and top with cashews.

What's great about this recipe ?			
"Easy-Fix"	✔	"Bone Health"	✔
"Quick-Fix"	✔	"Heart Health"	✔
"Easy-Chew"		"Sweetie"	
"Hands-on"		"High Fiber"	✔

SuperSource: copper, manganese, selenium

Nutrition information per serving: 188 calories, 26 g carbohydrates, 4 g protein, 7 g fat, 1 g saturated fat, 0 mg cholesterol, 100 mg sodium, 3 g fiber. Good source of vits. B1, B6, iron, magnesium, phosphorus.

Garlic Rice With Peppers and Pine Nuts

Servings: 4

A colorful, flavorful side dish that you can cook either of two ways – on the stovetop, or in the microwave. Recipe © USA Rice Federation.

1 small green pepper, cut into strips
1 small red pepper, cut into strips
1/4 cup pine nuts or slivered almonds
1 clove garlic, minced

1 tablespoon butter or margarine, melted
2 cups cooked brown rice (preferably cooked in chicken broth)
2 tablespoons chopped fresh parsley

1. Cook peppers, pine nuts, and garlic in butter in large skillet over medium-high heat until light brown. Add rice and parsley; stir until thoroughly heated.
2. To microwave: Combine peppers, pine nuts and butter in shallow 2-quart microproof baking dish. Cover and cook on HIGH 4 to 5 minutes; stir after 2 minutes. Stir in rice and parsley; cook on HIGH 1 minute or until thoroughly heated.

What's great about this recipe ?

"Easy-Fix"	✔	"Bone Health"	✔
"Quick-Fix"	✔	"Heart Health"	✔
"Easy-Chew"		"Sweetie"	
"Hands-on"		"High Fiber"	

SuperSource: Vit. C, manganese

Nutrition information per serving: 155 calories, 17 g carbohydrates, 4 g protein, 9 g fat, 3 g saturated fat, 8 mg cholesterol, 131 mg sodium, 2 g fiber. Good source of vits. B1, B6, iron, magnesium, phosphorus, copper.

Mexican Lime Rice

Servings: 6

This is a tangy and refreshing side dish for fish, meat, or vegetables.

1 cup brown rice
2 cups water or low sodium chicken broth
1/4 cup fresh lime juice

1/2 teaspoon salt
1/2 cup frozen peas
1 tablespoon grated lime rind
1 lime, cut in wedges, for serving

1. Cook rice in water or chicken broth, 2 tablespoons of the lime juice, and salt, about 35 - 60 minutes, depending on type of rice. Add frozen peas last 5 minutes of cooking.
2. Toss cooked hot rice with grated lime rind and remaining 2 tablespoons lime juice.
3. Serve with lime wedges.

What's great about this recipe ?

"Easy-Fix"	✔	"Bone Health"	
"Quick-Fix"		"Heart Health"	
"Easy-Chew"	✔	"Sweetie"	
"Hands-on"		"High Fiber"	✔

SuperSource: none

Nutrition information per serving: 127 calories, 25 g carbohydrates, 3 g protein, 2 g fat, 0 g saturated fat, 0 mg cholesterol, 219 mg sodium, 2 g fiber. Good source of chromium.

Cherry Rice Pilaf

Servings: 6

A tart, savory pilaf that will set off many main dishes. Use a food processor to do the chopping. Reprinted courtesy of Cherry Marketing Institute.

1 cup onion, chopped 1/2"
1 cup celery, chopped 1/2"
1/2 cup dried tart cherries
1 tablespoon chopped fresh thyme
  (or 1 teaspoon dried)
1 tablespoon chopped fresh marjoram
  (or 1 teaspoon dried)

1/2 teaspoon ground black pepper
1 tablespoon margarine
1/2 cup chopped walnuts
3 cups cooked brown rice, preferably
  long-grain

1. Put onion, celery, cherries, thyme, marjoram, pepper and margarine in a large nonstick skillet. Cook, uncovered, over medium heat 10 minutes, or until vegetables are tender, stirring occasionally. Add walnuts and cook 2 minutes longer. Add rice; heat and stir, mixing well. Cook 3 to 4 minutes, or until thoroughly heated.

What's great about this recipe ?

"Easy-Fix"	✔	"Bone Health"	✔
"Quick-Fix"	✔	"Heart Health"	✔
"Easy-Chew"	✔	"Sweetie"	
"Hands-on"		"High Fiber"	

SuperSource: Manganese, chromium

Nutrition information per serving: 186 calories, 25 g carbohydrates, 4 g protein, 9 g fat, 2 g saturated fat, 5 mg cholesterol, 139 mg sodium, 2 g fiber. Good source of vit. A, B1, B6, C, biotin, potassium, iron, magnesium, phosphorus, copper, selenium.

Baked Barley Casserole

Servings: 6

Whole raw almonds are a good source of fiber, trace minerals, and vitamin E. Use a food processor for the chopping and this recipe will be easy to prepare.

1 cup barley, soaked overnight
1 teaspoon butter
1/2 cup whole raw almonds
2 tablespoons olive oil
1 medium onion, finely chopped
1/4 cup green onion, thinly sliced
1 cup shredded carrot
1/4 teaspoon salt

1/4 teaspoon pepper
2 (14-ounce) cans low sodium chicken broth, undiluted, or 1 quart water and 2 chicken bouillon cubes
Parsley, for garnish

1. Preheat oven to 375 degrees F.
2. In frying pan over medium-low heat, melt butter. Add almonds and cook, stirring, until fragrant and lightly browned. Remove from pan and set aside.
3. Add olive oil to pan, and increase heat to medium. Cook onion, green onion, and carrot 2 minutes. Add soaked barley and saute until lightly browned. Stir in salt and pepper. Spoon into 1 1/2 quart casserole. Meantime, heat broth to boiling and pour over barley mixture. Stir to mix. Bake at 375ºF for 70 minutes, or until liquid is absorbed. Garnish with toasted almonds and parsley and serve immediately.

What's great about this recipe ?

"Easy-Fix"	✔	"Bone Health"	✔
"Quick-Fix"		"Heart Health"	✔
"Easy-Chew"	✔	"Sweetie"	
"Hands-on"		"High Fiber"	✔

SuperSource: Vit. A, copper, manganese, selenium, fiber

Nutrition information per serving: 240 calories, 29 g carbohydrates, 8 g protein, 12 g fat, 2 g saturated fat, 2 mg cholesterol, 137 mg sodium, 7 g fiber. Good source of vits. E, B1, B2, B3, potassium, iron, magnesium, phosphorus, zinc, chromium.

Quinoa Pilaf

Servings: 6

Quinoa is an old "new" grain. It was a staple food of the Incas, thousands of years ago. It contains a unique balance of complex carbohydrates, nutrients, and a high-quality protein. It also cooks quickly, a bonus!

1 cup quinoa
1 tablespoon olive oil
1 cup minced onion
1/2 cup diced bell pepper
2 teaspoons minced garlic
1/4 teaspoon turmeric

1 (14 ounce) can low sodium chicken
   broth, heated
1/4 teaspoon salt
1/4 cup pine nuts
2 tablespoons minced fresh parsley

1. Rinse quinoa under running cold water and drain well.
2. In a 2-quart saucepan over moderate heat, cook the onion and bell pepper in the oil until softened, about 4-6 minutes. Add the garlic and turmeric and cook, stirring, 1 minute more. Add the broth and salt, bring the liquid to a boil and simmer, covered, for 15 minutes. Remove pan from heat and let stand, covered, 5 minutes.
3. Meantime, in small skillet, over medium-low heat, cook and stir pine nuts until lightly browned. Remove from heat.
4. Fluff quinoa with a fork and spoon into serving dish. Garnish with pine nuts and parsley.

What's great about this recipe ?

"Easy-Fix"	✔	"Bone Health"	✔
"Quick-Fix"	✔	"Heart Health"	✔
"Easy-Chew"	✔	"Sweetie"	
"Hands-on"		"High Fiber"	✔

SuperSource: Iron, copper, manganese

Nutrition information per serving: 196 calories, 24 g carbohydrates, 7 g protein, 9 g fat, 1 g saturated fat, 0 mg cholesterol, 116 mg sodium, 3 g fiber. Good source of vits. B1, B2, C, potassium, magnesium, phosphorus, zinc, chromium.

Quinoa Salad

Servings: 6

A color-flecked, lemony salad, bursting with different flavors and textures. Can also be made with 3 cups of cooked brown rice.

1 cup quinoa
2 cups water
1/4 teaspoon salt
1 tomato, diced
1/2 cup red bell pepper, diced 1/2"
4 green onions, thinly sliced
1 stalk celery, diced 1/4"

Vinaigrette:
2 tablespoons lemon juice, preferably freshly squeezed
1/2 teaspoon minced garlic
1/4 teaspoon paprika
1/4 teaspoon salt
4 tablespoons sunflower oil
1/4 cup minced parsley or cilantro
1/4 cup sunflower seeds

1. Rinse quinoa well, and place in 2-quart saucepan with 2 cups water and salt and bring to a boil. Reduce heat to low and simmer, covered, for about 15-25 minutes, or until liquid is absorbed. Let stand for 5 minutes and fluff grains with a fork to separate. Allow to cool.
2. Meantime, prepare tomato, bell pepper, green onions, and celery. Whisk together lemon juice, garlic, paprika, salt, and oil. When quinoa is cool, stir in prepared vegetables. Pour vinaigrette over all, and toss to coat. Place in serving dish and garnish with parsley or cilantro and sunflower seeds. Serve at room temperature, or chilled.

What's great about this recipe ?

"Easy-Fix"		"Bone Health"	✔
"Quick-Fix"		"Heart Health"	✔
"Easy-Chew"		"Sweetie"	
"Hands-on"		"High Fiber"	

SuperSource: Vits. C, E, iron, copper, manganese

Nutrition information per serving: 212 calories, 24 g carbohydrates, 6 g protein, 11 g fat, 1 g saturated fat, 0 mg cholesterol, 209 mg sodium, 3 g fiber. Good source of vits. B1, B2, B6, pant.acid, potassium, magnesium, phosphorus, zinc, chromium, fiber.

Vegetables

Asian Broccoli

Servings: 4

Asian sesame oil has a unique taste; with the soy and garlic, it really sets this dish apart.

1 pound broccoli, rinsed, trimmed, and cut into florets (about 4 cups)

1 tablespoon reduced-sodium soy sauce
1 teaspoon Asian toasted sesame oil
1 large garlic clove, minced

1. In 4 quart pan, bring 3 quarts water to boil over high heat. Add broccoli and cook, uncovered, till just tender, about 5 minutes. Drain; plunge into ice water to chill. Drain again.
2. Meantime, in a small bowl, whisk together soy sauce, oil, and garlic. Let stand while broccoli cooks.
3. Place broccoli in serving bowl and toss with soy-oil mixture. Serve at room temperature, or chilled.

What's great about this recipe ?			
"Easy-Fix"	✔	"Bone Health"	✔
"Quick-Fix"	✔	"Heart Health"	✔
"Easy-Chew"		"Sweetie"	
"Hands-on"		"High Fiber"	✔

SuperSource: Vit. C, K, chromium, fiber

Nutrition information per serving: 45 calories, 7 g carbohydrates, 4 g protein, 2 g fat, 0 g saturated fat, 0 mg cholesterol, 180 mg sodium, 3 g fiber. Good source of vits. A, E, B2, B6, folate, pant.acid, potassium, iron, phosphorus, manganese.

Broccoli with Oil and Garlic

Servings: 4

Broccoli is a cancer-fighter, sunflower seed oil is rich in vitamin E, and garlic may help control cholesterol. What more could you ask of a delicious side dish?

1 pound broccoli
2 tablespoons sunflower oil
2 cloves garlic, minced

3 tablespoons lemon juice
1/4 teaspoon salt
Black pepper to taste

1. Wash broccoli. Cut off any woody parts at base of stems. Peel stems. Cut long or wide stalks in half.
2. Boil water in bottom of saucepan equipped with steamer or bring large pan of water to a boil. If steaming, put broccoli in steamer and cover tightly. Cook 8-12 minutes or til stems are just tender when pierced with point of knife. Remove from heat. If blanching, drop into boiling water and blanch til just tender, 5-6 minutes. Drain.
3. In small bowl, whisk oil, garlic, lemon juice, salt, and pepper. Drizzle over broccoli and toss gently to coat. Serve hot or cold.

What's great about this recipe ?			
"Easy-Fix"	✔	"Bone Health"	✔
"Quick-Fix"	✔	"Heart Health"	✔
"Easy-Chew"		"Sweetie"	
"Hands-on"		"High Fiber"	✔

SuperSource: Vits. C, E, K, chromium, fiber

Nutrition information per serving: 96 calories, 7 g carbohydrates, 4 g protein, 7 g fat, 1 g saturated fat, 0 mg cholesterol, 179 mg sodium, 3 g fiber. Good source of vits. A, B2, B6, folate, pant.acid, potassium, iron, phosphorus, manganese.

Roasted Brussels Sprouts

Servings: 4

Roasting vegetables changes the starches, slightly "caramelizing" them and creating a deep, smoky sweetness. The addition of the pecans and maple syrup makes for a dish that may win over those who always hated Brussels sprouts.

1 pound fresh Brussels sprouts	1 tablespoon butter
1 tablespoon olive oil	1/4 cup pecan halves
1/4 teaspoon salt	4 teaspoons maple syrup
1/4 teaspoon black pepper	

1. Preheat oven to 400 degrees F. Spray a heavy (preferably cast-iron) pan with cooking spray.
2. Wash sprouts and trim any tough outer leaves. In medium bowl, toss sprouts with olive oil, salt, and pepper. Spoon into pan and roast till just starting to blacken, about 15 - 20 minutes. Remove from oven.
3. Over medium heat, melt butter in a large skillet. Add pecans and saute till just fragrant, 2-3 minutes. Reduce heat to low, add maple syrup and sprouts, and saute till heated through, about 2 minutes more.

What's great about this recipe ?			
"Easy-Fix"	✔	"Bone Health"	✔
"Quick-Fix"	✔	"Heart Health"	✔
"Easy-Chew"		"Sweetie"	
"Hands-on"		"High Fiber"	✔

> **SuperSource: Vits. C, K, manganese, fiber**

Nutrition information per serving: 167 calories, 16 g carbohydrates, 4 g protein, 11 g fat, 3 g saturated fat, 8 mg cholesterol, 205 mg sodium, 5 g fiber. Good source of vits. A, B1, B6, E, folate, potassium, iron, phosphorus, copper.

Garlicky Spinach

Servings: 4

If you buy the prewashed baby spinach, preparation is a flash.* If chewing is a concern, chop the spinach before cooking.** Serving ideas: Place on plates, top with a fish steak or fillet. Or use as an omelet filling for a light meal.

2 tablespoons safflower oil
1 tablespoon garlic, minced

1 pound fresh spinach, stems removed
2 tablespoons lemon juice

1. In a large nonreactive pot, heat oil over moderately low heat. Add garlic and saute 1 minute. Add spinach by handfuls, stirring until it wilts, then adding another handful.
2. Remove pan from heat and stir in lemon juice. Transfer to serving bowl. Serve at once.

What's great about this recipe ?

"Easy-Fix"	✔	"Bone Health"	✔
"Quick-Fix"	✔*	"Heart Health"	✔
"Easy-Chew"	✔**	"Sweetie"	
"Hands-on"		"High Fiber"	✔

SuperSource: Vits. A, C, E, K, folate, biotin, iron, manganese, chromium, fiber

Nutrition information per serving: 92 calories, 6 g carbohydrates, 4 g protein, 7 g fat, 1 g saturated fat, 0 mg cholesterol, 92 mg sodium, 3 g fiber. Good source of vits. B2,B6, E, potassium, magnesium, copper.

Beans 'n Greens

Servings: 4

Greens are rich in antioxidants, magnesium, and vitamin A, while beans are full of fiber and minerals – a dynamic combination!

1 1/2 pounds kale, chard, or mustard greens, washed, trimmed, and cut in 1" pieces
2 teaspoons olive oil
2 cloves garlic, crushed
1 (15 ounce) can reduced-sodium white navy or Great Northern beans, undrained

6 dried tomato halves, rehydrated, chopped
1/2 cup chicken broth
1 teaspoon dried rosemary, crushed
1/4 teaspoon dried red pepper flakes
1/4 teaspoon salt
Black pepper, to taste

1. In large saucepan, bring 2 quarts water to boil. Add 1 tablespoon salt to water. Toss greens into boiling water; cook til almost tender but still bright green, 5-15 minutes (cooking time will depend on type of green). Drain and rinse with cold water. Set aside.

2. Meanwhile, heat olive oil in large skillet over moderately low heat. Saute garlic til tender but not browned. Stir in beans; cook and stir for 8 minutes, heating beans through (some beans may break up; this helps to thicken the dish).

3. Gently stir in reserved greens and remaining ingredients. Cook and stir gently til heated through.

What's great about this recipe ?

"Easy-Fix"	✔	"Bone Health"	✔
"Quick-Fix"	✔	"Heart Health"	✔
"Easy-Chew"	✔	"Sweetie"	
"Hands-on"		"High Fiber"	✔

SuperSource: Vits.A, B6, C, potassium, iron, magnesium, phosphorus, copper, manganese, selenium, chromium, fiber

Nutrition information per serving: 175 calories, 30 g carbohydrates, 11 g protein, 3 g fat, 0 g saturated fat, 0 mg cholesterol, 322 mg sodium, 9 g fiber. Good source of vits. B1, B2, B3, E, pant.acid, zinc.

Microwave Potatoes Lyonnaise

Servings: 6

Fast, easy, and delicious! Reprinted courtesy of The Idaho Potato Commission.

3 large baking potatoes, unpeeled and cubed 1/2"
2 small onions, diced 1/2"
2 tablespoons butter or margarine
2 cloves garlic, minced

1/2 teaspoon salt
1/8 teaspoon pepper
1/8 teaspoon paprika

1. Combine all ingredients in a deep 3-quart microwave-safe casserole dish.
2. Cover with microwaveable plastic wrap and microwave at HIGH 9 to 11 minutes, or until potatoes and onions are tender, stirring every 5 minutes. Let stand 5 minutes before serving.

What's great about this recipe ?			
"Easy-Fix"	✔	"Bone Health"	
"Quick-Fix"	✔	"Heart Health"	
"Easy-Chew"	✔	"Sweetie"	
"Hands-on"		"High Fiber"	✔

SuperSource: chromium, fiber

Nutrition information per serving: 125 calories, 21 g carbohydrates, 2 g protein, 4 g fat, 3 g saturated fat, 11 mg cholesterol, 240 mg sodium, 4 g fiber. Good source of vits. B6, C, potassium, copper.

Sweet Potatoes and Apples

Servings: 6

Peeling the sweet potatoes and apples makes them tender and easy to chew. However, it also removes fiber and some nutrients. If you prefer, leave them unpeeled.

Cooking spray
1 pound sweet potatoes, peeled and sliced 1/4 inch thick
2 tart cooking apples, peeled, halved, cored and sliced 1/4 inch thick

6 tablespoons pure maple syrup
1/3 cup apple juice
1 tablespoon butter
1/4 teaspoon salt

1. Preheat the oven to 350 degrees F. Spray a 10" pie pan with nonstick cooking spray. Arrange sweet potato and apple slices alternately in circular layers in pan.
2. In a medium saucepan, combine the maple syrup, apple juice, butter and salt. Simmer over moderate heat for 5 minutes. Pour half of the mixture over the slices in the baking dish and cover the dish securely with foil.
3. Bake in the center of the oven for 40 minutes, or until the apples release their liquid. Remove from the oven, uncover and baste the apples and sweet potatoes with the pan juices. Increase the oven temperature to 450º and place the dishes in the upper third of the oven. Continue baking for about 35 minutes longer, basting a few more times, until the sweet potatoes are tender and nicely glazed. Serve hot or at room temperature.

What's great about this recipe ?

"Easy-Fix"	✔	"Bone Health"	
"Quick-Fix"		"Heart Health"	
"Easy-Chew"	✔	"Sweetie"	✔
"Hands-on"		"High Fiber"	

SuperSource: Vit. A

Nutrition information per serving: 177 calories, 36 g carbohydrates, 1 g protein, 4 g fat, 2 g saturated fat, 5 mg cholesterol, 160 mg sodium, 2 g fiber. Good source of vit. C, iron, copper, manganese, chromium.

Roasted Sweet Potato Wedges

Servings: 4

These are easy, and delicious – the oven-roasting brings out the sweetness. You can leave the wedges unpeeled, and peel after roasting – or eat the peel for extra fiber. These can also be served at room temperature, picked up, and eaten out of hand.*

Nonstick cooking spray
4 medium sweet potatoes, peeled and cut lengthwise into 8 wedges each

2 tablespoons olive oil
1/4 teaspoon salt
Pepper
½ teaspoon crumbled dried rosemary

1. Preheat the oven to 375º. Spray baking sheet with cooking spray.
2. In medium bowl, toss the potato wedges with the oil, salt, pepper, and rosemary. Lay the wedges on their side, and roast for about 25 minutes, turning once, until tender and lightly browned.

What's great about this recipe ?

"Easy-Fix"	✔	"Bone Health"	
"Quick-Fix"	✔	"Heart Health"	✔
"Easy-Chew"	✔	"Sweetie"	
"Hands-on"	✔*	"High Fiber"	✔

SuperSource: Vit. A, C, copper, manganese, fiber

Nutrition information per serving: 177 calories, 28 g carbohydrates, 2 g protein, 7 g fat, 1 g saturated fat, 0 mg cholesterol, 157 mg sodium, 3 g fiber. Good source of vits. B2, B6, pant.acid, biotin, potassium.

Acorn Squash with Fruit and Nuts

Servings: 2

Microwaving makes this a super-quick dish. The squash halves make their own bowls, full of delicious fruits and nuts.

1 acorn squash	2 tablespoons dried cranberries
3 tablespoons brown sugar	1 tablespoon butter, melted
2 tablespoons chopped walnuts	1/4 teaspoon salt
2 tablespoons seedless raisins	

1. Cut squash in half lengthwise; remove seeds. Microwave squash 8 minutes, turning every two minutes, till fork-tender.
2. Combine brown sugar, nuts, raisins, cranberries, butter and salt; divide equally between squash halves. Microwave at HIGH (100%) 30 seconds or until thoroughly heated and lightly glazed.

What's great about this recipe ?

"Easy-Fix"	✔	"Bone Health"	✔
"Quick-Fix"	✔	"Heart Health"	✔
"Easy-Chew"		"Sweetie"	✔
"Hands-on"		"High Fiber"	✔

SuperSource: Vit. B1, potassium, iron, copper, fiber

Nutrition information per serving: 296 calories, 53 g carbohydrates, 3 g protein, 10 g fat, 4 g saturated fat, 16 mg cholesterol, 223 mg sodium, 8 g fiber. Good source of vits. A, B6, C, pant.acid, magnesium, phosphorus, manganese.

Ratatouille on a Couch

Servings: 4

I often make this dish for company dinners; it takes time to prepare, but it's well worth the effort. It's also easy to chew.

1/4 cup chopped onion
2 cloves garlic, minced
2 teaspoons olive oil
3 tomatoes, diced
2 teaspoons dried oregano, crumbled
1/2 teaspoon pepper
1 bay leaf
1 eggplant (3/4 Lb), pared and diced
2 small zucchini, diced
1 green bell pepper, chopped
1/2 pound mushrooms, chopped

1 tablespoon chives
1 tablespoon grated Parmesan cheese
Polenta:
1 3/4-2 cups water
3/4 cup yellow corn meal, preferably whole (with bran and germ)
1/2 cup cold water
1/2 teaspoon salt
1/2 cup grated Cheddar cheese

1. Saute onion and garlic in oil in large skillet, stirring often, til tender, about 2 minutes. Add tomatoes, oregano, pepper and bay leaf; cover; simmer 5 minutes. Add eggplant, zucchini, bell pepper and mushrooms, stirring well. Cover and simmer 5 minutes longer. Stir in chives and Parmesan.
2. Meanwhile, bring 1 3/4 cups water to a boil. In small bowl, combine corn meal, cold water and salt. Add to rapidly boiling water, lower heat, and beat with wire whisk while it cooks until thick, about 10 minutes.
3. Stir in cheese. Spread polenta evenly on large serving platter. Top with ratatouille.

What's great about this recipe ?			
"Easy-Fix"		"Bone Health"	✔
"Quick-Fix"		"Heart Health"	✔
"Easy-Chew"	✔	"Sweetie"	
"Hands-on"		"High Fiber"	✔

> **SuperSource: Vits. B1, B2, B3, B6, C, K, pant.acid, potassium, iron, phosphorus, copper, chromium, fiber**

Nutrition information per serving: 257 calories, 38 g carbohydrates, 11 g protein, 9 g fat, 4 g saturated fat, 16 mg cholesterol, 279 mg sodium, 8 g fiber. Good source of vits. A, folate, calcium, magnesium, zinc, manganese, selenium.

Microwave Glazed Carrots, Apples, and Zucchini

Servings: 5

Do the slicing in a food processor. Quick, easy, and satisfying to the sweet tooth. Reprinted courtesy of Monitor Sugar.

2 cups carrots, thinly sliced diagonally
6 dried figs, chopped 1/4"
1 cup zucchini, thinly sliced
1 1/2 cups apple, thinly sliced

2 tablespoons brown sugar
1 teaspoon cornstarch
1/2 teaspoon ground cinnamon
2 teaspoons butter

1. Combine carrots, figs, and zucchini in a 1-quart microwave dish; pour in 3 tablespoons water. Cook covered on HIGH for 3 minutes or until carrots are crisp-tender. Drain; then gently toss apples into the vegetable mixture.

2. In a small mixing bowl, combine brown sugar, cornstarch, cinnamon, and cut in butter with fork. Sprinkle mixture over top of apple-vegetable mixture. Cover and microwave on HIGH for 3 minutes. Gently toss mixture, coating apples and vegetables with the glaze; cook uncovered 2-3 minutes or until glaze thickens.

What's great about this recipe ?

"Easy-Fix"	✔	"Bone Health"	
"Quick-Fix"	✔	"Heart Health"	✔
"Easy-Chew"	✔	"Sweetie"	✔
"Hands-on"		"High Fiber"	✔

SuperSource: Vit. A, manganese, chromium, fiber

Nutrition information per serving: 146 calories, 33 g carbohydrates, 2 g protein, 2 g fat, 1 g saturated fat, 4 mg cholesterol, 61 mg sodium, 6 g fiber. Good source of vit. B6, potassium, iron, copper.

Green Beans and Walnuts in Vinaigrette

Servings: 6

Select the wide Italian or "pole beans" whenever possible, they are much more flavorful. You can use bottled minced garlic to speed preparation.

1 pound Italian green beans, rinsed, stem ends trimmed
1/2 cup walnut halves
1 tablespoon olive oil
1/4 teaspoon salt
Black pepper to taste
Dressing:
1/4 cup white wine vinegar

2 teaspoons sugar
1/2 teaspoon dried oregano
1 teaspoon minced garlic
1/4 teaspoon salt
Black pepper to taste
2 tablespoons sunflower oil
1/4 cup red onion, diced
2 tablespoons feta cheese, crumbled

1. Preheat oven to 450 degrees F. Snap off tips of beans at the stem end; place beans and nuts in single layer on a baking sheet. Drizzle with olive oil; sprinkle with salt and pepper. Toss to coat. Roast beans in lower half of oven 5 minutes; stir and roast 5 more minutes.
2. In a large bowl, whisk together vinegar, sugar, oregano, garlic, salt, and pepper. Whisk in sunflower oil; add onion.
3. Toss roasted beans and walnuts with dressing; spoon into serving dish. Sprinkle beans with crumbled feta; serve warm or at room temperature.

What's great about this recipe ?

"Easy-Fix"	✔	"Bone Health"	✔
"Quick-Fix"	✔	"Heart Health"	✔
"Easy-Chew"		"Sweetie"	
"Hands-on"		"High Fiber"	✔

SuperSource: chromium, fiber

Nutrition information per serving: 171 calories, 10 g carbohydrates, 4 g protein, 14 g fat, 2 g saturated fat, 4 mg cholesterol, 250 mg sodium, 3 g fiber. Good source of vits. K, biotin, iron, phosphorus, copper, manganese.

Asparagus Dijon

Servings: 4

Asparagus is so good, it doesn't need fancy sauces. Just a dash of good olive oil, some lemon juice, and a bit of good-quality Dijon mustard.

1 pound fresh asparagus, washed
   and trimmed
1 tablespoon sunflower oil
2 tablespoons lemon juice
   (preferably fresh)

1 teaspoon Dijon mustard
1/8 teaspoon salt

1. Place asparagus on steamer rack in pot; cover tightly and steam until tender; about 8-10 minutes depending on thickness of spears. Drain and place on serving platter. In small bowl, whisk together the oil, lemon juice, mustard, and salt. Drizzle over asparagus; serve warm or at room temperature.

What's great about this recipe ?

"Easy-Fix"	✔	"Bone Health"	
"Quick-Fix"	✔	"Heart Health"	✔
"Easy-Chew"		"Sweetie"	
"Hands-on"		"High Fiber"	

SuperSource: Vits. C, K, folate

Nutrition information per serving: 59 calories, 3 g carbohydrates, 3 g protein, 4 g fat, 1 g saturated fat, 0 mg cholesterol, 95 mg sodium, 1 g fiber. Good source of vits. B1, B2, B6, E, copper, fiber.

Savory Beets

Servings: 4

Besides adding a bright dash of color to your meal, these sweet-sour beets are delicious, too! Reprinted courtesy of The National Honey Board.

2 tablespoons finely chopped onion
1 tablespoon butter
3 tablespoons honey

2 tablespoons wine vinegar
1/8 teaspoon ground cloves
1 16-ounce can sliced beets, drained

1. Sauté onion in butter in large skillet over medium heat until softened. Add honey, vinegar, and cloves; cook and stir until mixture begins to boil.
2. Add beets; cook until thoroughly heated.

What's great about this recipe ?			
"Easy-Fix"	✔	"Bone Health"	
"Quick-Fix"	✔	"Heart Health"	
"Easy-Chew"	✔	"Sweetie"	
"Hands-on"		"High Fiber"	✔

SuperSource: iron, fiber

Nutrition information per serving: 112 calories, 22 g carbohydrates, 1 g protein, 3 g fat, 2 g saturated fat, 8 mg cholesterol, 252 mg sodium, 2 g fiber. Good source of manganese.

Flash Primavera

Servings: 8 side dish or 4 main dish

This dish can be a meal in itself. Cooking the pasta and vegetable together saves both time and cleanup. Reprinted courtesy of the National Pasta Association.

1 pound mostaccioli, ziti or other medium pasta shape, uncooked

1 head broccoli or cauliflower, cut into small florets (1 1/2 pounds)

1 tablespoon cornstarch

1/4 cup water

3 cloves garlic, minced

1 (15 1/2-ounce) can low-sodium chicken broth

1 10-ounce package frozen mixed vegetables, thawed

1 10-ounce package frozen chopped spinach, thawed

Salt and pepper, to taste

1 cup grated Parmesan cheese

1. Prepare pasta according to package directions. Five minutes before the pasta is done, stir in the broccoli or cauliflower. Drain pasta and vegetables and transfer to a large bowl.

2. In a small bowl, dissolve the cornstarch in 1/4 cup of water. Put the garlic in a large saucepan with chicken broth. Simmer over medium heat for 3 minutes. Whisk in the cornstarch. Stir in the mixed vegetables and spinach and cook until hot, about 5 minutes. Toss the sauce and vegetables with the pasta, season with salt and pepper and sprinkle with Parmesan cheese and serve.

What's great about this recipe ?			
"Easy-Fix"	✔	"Bone Health"	✔
"Quick-Fix"	✔	"Heart Health"	✔
"Easy-Chew"	✔	"Sweetie"	
"Hands-on"		"High Fiber"	✔

SuperSource: Vits. A, B1, B2, C, K, iron, manganese, fiber

Nutrition information per serving (8 servings): 331 calories, 50 g carbohydrates, 16 g protein, 7 g fat, 3 g saturated fat, 74 mg cholesterol, 334 mg sodium, 6 g fiber. Good source of vits. B3, B6, folate, pant.acid, potassium, calcium, magnesium, phosphorus, copper.

Green Bean Almond Rice

Servings: 8

Having the rice already cooked and frozen will make this extra-easy. Just thaw the rice and stir into the skillet. Recipe © USA Rice Federation.

1 tablespoon butter or margarine
1/2 cup chopped onion
1/3 cup chopped red bell pepper
1/2 cup slivered almonds
3 cups cooked brown rice (preferably cooked in chicken broth)

1 (10 ounce) package frozen French-style green beans, thawed
1/8 teaspoon ground white pepper, or to taste
1/4 teaspoon tarragon

1. Melt butter in large skillet over medium-high heat. Add onion and red pepper; cook 4-6 minutes or until tender. Add almonds; stir until lightly browned, about 2 minutes. Add rice, green beans, white pepper and tarragon. Cook and stir until heated through and blended.

What's great about this recipe ?			
"Easy-Fix"	✔	"Bone Health"	✔
"Quick-Fix"	✔	"Heart Health"	✔
"Easy-Chew"		"Sweetie"	
"Hands-on"		"High Fiber"	✔

SuperSource: manganese, selenium, chromium, fiber

Nutrition information per serving: 160 calories, 22 g carbohydrates, 4 g protein, 7 g fat, 2 g saturated fat, 4 mg cholesterol, 21 mg sodium, 4 g fiber. Good source of vits. B6, C, E, iron, magnesium, phosphorus, copper.

Southwest Corn and Bean Dish

Servings: 4 side dish or 2 main dish

Serve with whole-wheat tortillas, a bit of cheese, and a piece of fruit, for a complete meal. Reprinted courtesy of Ontario White Bean Producers.

1 (15 ounce) can reduced-sodium white pea beans
2 cups frozen corn, thawed
3/4 cup red bell pepper, diced
3/4 cup medium or hot chunky salsa
Juice of one lime

1 tablespoon sunflower oil
1 stalk celery, diced
2 green onions, finely chopped
1 teaspoon ground cumin
1/4 cup chopped cilantro

1. In a large non-reactive bowl, combine all ingredients except the cilantro. Chill in the refrigerator for at least 3 hours or overnight.
2. Just before serving, mix in the fresh cilantro. Garnish with additional sprigs of cilantro and serve.

What's great about this recipe ?

"Easy-Fix"	✔	"Bone Health"	
"Quick-Fix"	✔	"Heart Health"	✔
"Easy-Chew"		"Sweetie"	
"Hands-on"		"High Fiber"	✔

SuperSource: Vit. C, iron, chromium, fiber

Nutrition information per serving: 176 calories, 35 g carbohydrates, 11 g protein, 4 g fat, 1 g saturated fat, 0 mg cholesterol, 350 mg sodium, 9 g fiber. Good source of vits. B6, E, biotin, potassium.

Fruit Dishes

Blueberry & Tortellini Fruit Salad
Servings: 6

This is a quick and refreshing salad you can throw together at a moment's notice. Three-cheese tortellini pasta is found in the refrigerated section of your grocery store. Various other fruits such as bananas, peaches, apples, and oranges may be used. Reprinted courtesy of the North American Blueberry Council.

1 (9 ounce) package three-cheese tortellini pasta
1 cup fresh blueberries
1 cup sliced fresh strawberries
1 (11 ounce) can Mandarin Orange segments, drained

3/4 cup green seedless grapes
1/4 cup sliced almonds
1/2 cup purchased lowfat poppy seed dressing

1. Cook pasta according to directions on package; drain. In a large bowl, combine pasta, blueberries, strawberries, oranges, grapes, and almonds. Pour dressing over salad and toss lightly; refrigerate until ready to serve.

What's great about this recipe ?			
"Easy-Fix"	✔	"Bone Health"	
"Quick-Fix"	✔	"Heart Health"	✔
"Easy-Chew"		"Sweetie"	✔
"Hands-on"		"High Fiber"	

SuperSource: Vit. C

Nutrition information per serving: 325 calories, 35 g carbohydrates, 10 g protein, 10 g fat, 3 g saturated fat, 26 mg cholesterol, 336 mg sodium, 4 g fiber. Good source of vits. E, iron, magnesium, copper, fiber.

Fabulous Fruit Salad

Servings: 4

You can vary the ingredients according to the season – try pears, kiwi, dried cherries for a change. Do the chopping in a food processor. Recipe provided by www.Allrecipes.com, the world's favorite recipe web site. All rights reserved. Copyright 2002 Allrecipes.com Recipe submitted by: Tracy Fall.

1 red apple, cored and chopped
1 Granny Smith apple, cored and chopped
1 nectarine, pitted and sliced
2 stalks celery, chopped 1/4"

1/2 cup dried cranberries
1/2 cup chopped walnuts
1 (8 ounce) container lowfat lemon yogurt

1. In a large bowl, combine red apple, Granny Smith apple, nectarine, celery, dried cranberries, and walnuts. Mix in yogurt. Chill until ready to serve.

What's great about this recipe ?

"Easy-Fix"	✔	"Bone Health"	
"Quick-Fix"	✔	"Heart Health"	✔
"Easy-Chew"		"Sweetie"	✔
"Hands-on"		"High Fiber"	✔

SuperSource: copper, chromium, fiber

Nutrition information per serving: 223 calories, 30 g carbohydrates, 5 g protein, 11 g fat, 1 g saturated fat, 4 mg cholesterol, 59 mg sodium, 5 g fiber. Good source of vit. C, biotin, potassium, manganese.

Gingered Fruit

Servings: 2

Ginger can help relieve nausea. This recipe is a good one to eat just before taking levodopa – protein is minimal, so it will not interfere with levodopa absorption, yet the food plus ginger may help settle the stomach. For difficulty chewing, chop or grate the fruits finely.*

2 tablespoons honey
2 tablespoons lemon juice
1 apple, cored
1 pear, cored

1 kiwi, peeled
1 tablespoon chopped crystallized ginger, or 1/4 teaspoon ground ginger

1. In food processor, combine honey and lemon juice. Drop in fruits and ginger, and coarsely chop with on-off pulses. Serve at once.

What's great about this recipe ?

"Easy-Fix"	✔	"Bone Health"	
"Quick-Fix"	✔	"Heart Health"	✔
"Easy-Chew"	✔*	"Sweetie"	✔
"Hands-on"		"High Fiber"	✔

SuperSource: Vit. C, iron, chromium, fiber

Nutrition information per serving: 205 calories, 53 g carbohydrates, 1 g protein, 1 g fat, 0 g saturated fat, 0 mg cholesterol, 7 mg sodium, 5 g fiber. Good source of potassium, copper.

Roasted Gingered Apples and Figs

Servings: 4

This is a versatile dish. It's a tart accompaniment to meats or poultry; but it's also good as a breakfast dish with vanilla yogurt and granola. If chewing is difficult, peel and chop the apples before cooking, chop the figs and cranberries 1/4" and omit almonds.*

Nonstick cooking spray
4 baking apples
4 dried figs, chopped ½"
2 tablespoons dried cranberries
1/4 cup honey
1/4 cup calcium-fortified orange juice

1 tablespoon lemon juice
1 tablespoon crystallized ginger, chopped fine
1/3 cup hot water
1/4 cup slivered almonds

1. Preheat oven to 400 degrees F. Spray baking dish with cooking spray. Quarter apples and remove core. Place apples, figs, and cranberries in prepared baking dish.
2. Combine honey, orange juice, lemon juice, and ginger; mix well. Spoon over apple mixture, coating them well. Pour hot water into baking dish. Cover with lid or aluminum foil. Bake 15 minutes. Remove cover and bake 30 minutes longer or until apples and figs are glazed and tender; baste with liquid from baking dish every 10 minutes. Remove from oven and sprinkle with almonds to serve.

What's great about this recipe ?

"Easy-Fix"	✔	"Bone Health"	
"Quick-Fix"		"Heart Health"	✔
"Easy-Chew"	✔*	"Sweetie"	✔
"Hands-on"		"High Fiber"	✔

SuperSource: Chromium, fiber

Nutrition information per serving: 253 calories, 55 g carbohydrates, 2 g protein, 5 g fat, 1 g saturated fat, 0 mg cholesterol, 5 mg sodium, 6 g fiber. Good source of vits. C, E, biotin, potassium, iron, phosphorus, copper, manganese.

Spiced Dried Fruit Compote

Servings: 6

Dried fruits are a real convenience food. They can be stored indefinitely, and are always available for a tasty side dish. This is a good breakfast starter, but also accompanies meats and poultry well. You can use any dried fruits, such as peaches, cherries, dates, cranberries, etc. If constipation is a concern, be sure to include prunes and figs. If chewing is difficult, chop the cooked fruits 1/4".*

1/4 cup honey
1 1/2 cups calcium-fortified orange juice
1 tablespoon grated orange peel
1/2 cup dried figs
1/2 cup dried prunes
1/4 cup dried apricots

1/4 cup dried pears
1/4 cup dried apples
1/4 cup raisins
1/2 teaspoon ground cinnamon
1/4 teaspoon ground cloves
1/4 teaspoon ground ginger
1/2 cup dry red wine (optional)

1. Combine honey, orange juice and orange peel in large saucepan. Bring to a boil over medium-high heat. Add fruit. Add cinnamon, cloves, and ginger. Reduce heat to low; simmer 5 minutes. Remove from heat; add wine.
2. Let stand in refrigerator overnight to allow flavors to blend. Serve warm or cold. Store leftovers in refrigerator; keeps well for 3 days.

What's great about this recipe ?

"Easy-Fix"	✔	"Bone Health"	
"Quick-Fix"		"Heart Health"	✔
"Easy-Chew"	✔*	"Sweetie"	✔
"Hands-on"		"High Fiber"	✔

SuperSource: Fiber

Nutrition information per serving: 214 calories, 53 g carbohydrates, 2 g protein, 0 g fat, 0 g saturated fat, 0 mg cholesterol, 9 mg sodium, 4 g fiber. Good source of vit. C, potassium, iron, copper, manganese.

SOUPS, SALADS, & SANDWICHES

What's more satisfying than a bowl of hot soup, especially on a cold day? Or a bowl of chilled soup on a hot day! Or a well-stuffed sandwich, or a hearty salad, anytime. Many of the recipes here are a whole meal, all by themselves, combining grains, vegetables, and proteins in a single dish.

Soups are eaten and beloved around the world; and they can be excellent dishes for those with PD. Most can be pureed – and diluted or thickened, if need be – for those who may have difficulty chewing.

> Another good point: a pureed soup can be sipped from a mug, it doesn't need to be spooned up from a bowl; so if it's too time-consuming to deal with eating utensils, your loved one may get more nourishment from a mug of soup than spending hours trying to deal with forks and knives. There are some refreshing chilled soups, too, for hot summer days. Gazpacho, for example, is a "sippable salad."

The _salads_ I've selected are mostly those that can serve either as a side dish, or in some cases even a meal. You'll notice that I haven't included tossed green salads. This is because tossed salads may require the diner to cut the greens, stab them with the fork, and convey them to the mouth, which, in advanced PD, can be difficult and time-consuming. The time would be better spent eating more nutrient-dense foods. Some of the filling main-dish salads here can be eaten with a spoon, if that's easier than using a fork.

> Tip: If green salads are a favorite, but it's difficult getting them on the fork, consider shredding the greens about 1/4" wide, then chopping them into 1" lengths. Toss with shredded vegetables, then with a thick dressing to bind the ingredients, and you'll find the salad will be much easier to manage.

A _sandwich_ is a portable meal – it can be packed and taken with you wherever you need to go. The playing field is leveled, because _no one_ needs any eating utensils.

A sandwich is a true "convenience food." It can also be cut into small "mini-sandwiches" to make them even easier to manage. It may help to enclose it in waxed paper or aluminum foil, to keep the ingredients from sliding out.

> If chewing is a problem, consider sandwiches that contain ground or chopped foods, such as minced chicken or egg. Mix these with some chopped pickle and plenty of mayonnaise to make the filling moister and easier to chew.

If you have a sandwich maker you can create hot sealed sandwiches that are easy to handle as well as delicious. Place two slices of whole-grain bread in the sandwich maker and add your choice of fillings – scrambled egg; crumbled cooked sausage or ground beef with gravy; tuna salad; cheese; even some of the salads included here can be used as a filling.

> Tip – for a "breakfast sandwich" stir up pancake batter, add some cooked ground ham or sausage or shredded cheese, and make small hot cakes. Roll these up and place on a tray at breakfast time, so everyone can help themselves – no forks required, but you could add a bowl of maple syrup for dipping.

Soups

Vegetable-Beef-Barley Crockery Stew

Servings: 8

You can often buy precut beef chunks; also bottled minced garlic. These will hasten preparation time. Then, just turn on the crockery cooker, sit back and relax! But feel free to pile everything into a large pot and cook it on the stovetop, if you'd like it to be ready sooner. If chewing is a concern, dice the meat 1/2."*

1 cup soaked, drained, uncooked hulled barley
1 pound beef stew meat, fat trimmed, cut in 1" chunks
1 small bell pepper, chopped
1 cup fresh or frozen thawed green beans, cut 1"
1 cup chopped onion
3 large carrots, cut in 1/2" chunks
1 teaspoon minced garlic

1 teaspoon salt
1/2 teaspoon dried thyme leaves
1 bay leaf
1/4 teaspoon pepper
4 1/2 cups water
2 cans (14 1/2 ounces each) reduced-sodium tomatoes, undrained
1 can (8 ounces) tomato sauce

1. Presoak hulled barley at least 4 hours, or overnight. Drain. Mix all ingredients in 3 1/2- to 6-quart slow cooker.
2. Cover and cook on low heat setting 8 to 9 hours (or high heat setting 4 to 5 hours) or until vegetables and barley are tender. Remove bay leaf.
3. Leftovers may be frozen if desired.

What's great about this recipe ?			
"Easy-Fix"	✔	"Bone Health"	✔
"Quick-Fix"		"Heart Health"	✔
"Easy-Chew"	✔*	"Sweetie"	
"Hands-on"		"High Fiber"	✔

SuperSource: Vits, A, B1, B3, B6, B12, C, potassium, iron, phosphorus, zinc, copper, manganese, selenium, chromium, fiber

Nutrition information per serving: 251 calories, 34 g carbohydrates, 19 g protein, 5 g fat, 2 g saturated fat, 28 mg cholesterol, 337 mg sodium, 8 g fiber. Good source of vits. E, B2, magnesium.

Vegetable Soup with Ground Beef

Servings: 4

Another excellent beef-vegetable soup; this one made with ground beef, so it's easier to chew. Can be made in a Dutch oven; or started in a skillet, then transferred to a crockery cooker. See *Side Dishes* for instructions on cooking barley

Cooking spray
8 ounces lean ground beef
½ cup chopped onion
1 clove garlic, minced
1 cup chopped cabbage
1 1/2 cups cooked barley
1 1/2 cups water
1 teaspoon Italian seasoning

1 cup chopped celery
1 cup chopped zucchini
1 (28 ounce) can whole tomatoes with juices, chopped
1 (8 ounce) can white beans, undrained
1 (8 ounce) can whole kernel corn, undrained

1. Spray large pot with cooking spray. Brown ground beef over medium heat; add onion and garlic, and cook, stirring, until beef is no longer pink. Drain off any fat.
2. Stir in cabbage, barley, water, Italian seasoning, celery, zucchini, tomatoes, beans, and corn. Heat to a boil; reduce heat to low. Cover pot and simmer 30 minutes, stirring occasionally, or until vegetables are tender.

What's great about this recipe ?			
"Easy-Fix"		"Bone Health"	✔
"Quick-Fix"		"Heart Health"	✔
"Easy-Chew"	✔	"Sweetie"	
"Hands-on"		"High Fiber"	✔

SuperSource: Vits. B1, B3, B6, B12, C, K, potassium, iron, phosphorus, zinc, copper, manganese, selenium, chromium, fiber

Nutrition information per serving: 372 calories, 50 g carbohydrates, 21 g protein, 13 g fat, 5 g saturated fat, 43 mg cholesterol, 449 mg sodium, 12 g fiber. Good source of vits. A, B2, folate, pantothenic acid, biotin, magnesium.

Sausage-Tomato Stew with Beans 'n Greens

Servings: 4

Mmm-m-m-m...what a terrific way to eat your greens! Add a slice of buttered whole wheat bread and perhaps a bit of cheese to round out the meal.

2 tablespoons olive or soy oil
4 ounces mild sausage, casings removed; or chorizo or pepperoni
2 onions, chopped
2 carrots, chopped
3 cloves garlic, minced
1 pound kale or spinach, tough stems removed, washed well and chopped 1/2"

1 (15 ounce) can diced tomatoes with juice
4 cups water
1/4 teaspoon salt
1/2 teaspoon black pepper
2 (19-ounce) cans white beans, drained and rinsed

1. In a 4-quart pot, heat 1 tablespoon oil over medium heat. Add sausage and cook, crumbling with spoon, until brown, about 4 minutes. Add remaining oil to pan and cook onions, stirring, until onions soften, about 4-5 minutes.
2. Add carrot, garlic and kale to the pan and cook, stirring, until the kale wilts, about 4 minutes. Stir in tomatoes, water, salt, and pepper; bring to a simmer, and cook, covered, until the carrot and kale are tender, about 20-25 minutes.
3. Stir in beans and cook until warmed through, about 5 minutes.

What's great about this recipe ?

"Easy-Fix"	✔	"Bone Health"	✔
"Quick-Fix"		"Heart Health"	✔
"Easy-Chew"	✔	"Sweetie"	
"Hands-on"		"High Fiber"	✔

SuperSource: Vit. A, B1, B6, C, K, potassium, iron, copper, manganese, chromium, fiber

Nutrition information per serving: 462 calories, 56 g carbohydrates, 20 g protein, 17 g fat, 4 g saturated fat, 24 mg cholesterol, 570 mg sodium, 15 g fiber. Good source of vits. B2, B3, B12, E, pant.acid, calcium, magnesium, phosphorus, zinc.

Chicken and Rice Soup

Servings: 2

Use the precooked frozen brown rice (see "Side Dishes") and a food processor to shred and chop* while the broth comes to a boil; this recipe will go together like lightning!

3 cups reduced-sodium chicken broth
1 carrot, shredded
1 stalk celery, diced
1 medium onion, chopped
1 cup frozen peas

1/4 teaspoon black pepper
1 tablespoon dried parsley
1 cup cooked brown rice
1 (5 ounce) can chunk chicken in water

1. Bring broth to a boil over high heat. Add carrot, celery, onion, peas, pepper, and parsley. Reduce heat to simmer, cover and cook for 20 minutes, or until vegetables are tender. Add rice and chicken, and simmer 5 minutes longer or till heated through. Serve at once.

What's great about this recipe ?

"Easy-Fix"	✔*	"Bone Health"	✔
"Quick-Fix"	✔*	"Heart Health"	✔
"Easy-Chew"	✔	"Sweetie"	
"Hands-on"		"High Fiber"	✔

SuperSource: Vits. A, B1, B6, iron, phosphorus, copper, manganese, selenium, chromium, fiber

Nutrition information per serving: 352 calories, 47 g carbohydrates, 27 g protein, 8 g fat, 3 g saturated fat, 35 mg cholesterol, 295 mg sodium, 9 g fiber. Good source of vits. B2, B3, C, K, folate, pant.acid, potassium, magnesium, zinc.

Chicken Chili

Serves 6

Try chicken and bulghur instead of chicken and noodles for a change and see how it boosts the fiber! Use a food processor to ease the chopping and shredding.*

8 ounces canned tomato juice
1 cup bulghur (cracked wheat)
2 tablespoons peanut or safflower oil
2 medium onions, chopped
4 garlic cloves, minced
3 celery stalks, diced 1/4"
3 carrots, shredded
1 (14 ounce) can Italian plum tomatoes, with juices
1 (15.5 ounce) can pinto beans

1 (12.5 ounce) can chunk chicken in water, drained
1 (4 ounce) can green chilies, chopped
1/3 cup chili powder, or to taste
2 teaspoons ground cumin
1 teaspoon dried oregano
½ teaspoon black pepper
12 ounces beer or water

1. In small saucepan, heat tomato juice over medium heat to boiling. Remove from heat and add bulghur. Cover and let stand 10 minutes.
2. Meantime, in large 5-6 quart pot, heat oil over medium heat. Add onion and garlic and cook 3-4 minutes or til soft. Add celery, carrot, and tomatoes with juice, mashing tomatoes with metal spoon. Cover and cook til vegetables are almost tender, about 20 minutes.
3. Add pinto beans, bulghur, chicken, chilies, chili powder, cumin, oregano, pepper, and beer or water. Simmer, partly covered, 30 minutes, stirring occasionally to prevent sticking.

What's great about this recipe ?			
"Easy-Fix"	✔*	"Bone Health"	✔
"Quick-Fix"		"Heart Health"	✔
"Easy-Chew"	✔	"Sweetie"	
"Hands-on"		"High Fiber"	✔

SuperSource: Vits. A, B3, B6, C, pant.acid, potassium, iron, phosphorus, copper, chromium, fiber

Nutrition information per serving: 404 calories, 54 g carbohydrates, 23 g protein, 10 g fat, 2 g saturated fat, 37 mg cholesterol, 415 mg sodium, 12 g fiber. Good source of vits. B1, B2, E, K, folate, zinc, manganese, selenium.

Turkey, Mushroom, and Lentil Soup

Servings: 4

This is an excellent way to use up leftover turkey; but canned chicken or turkey will work, too. Consider using pre-sliced fresh mushrooms; or, in a pinch, a 4-ounce can of sliced mushrooms. Notice how adding legumes, such as lentils, increases nutrients like folate, potassium, magnesium, and fiber.

Cooking spray
2 tablespoons olive oil
1 onion, chopped
8 ounces fresh mushrooms, sliced
2 cloves garlic, minced
1 cup green lentils, rinsed well
1/2 teaspoon salt
6 cups water

6 ounces cooked turkey, cubed ½"; or 1 (5 ounce) can chunk chicken
1/4 teaspoon fresh-ground black pepper
1 tablespoon reduced-sodium soy sauce
1/4 cup plus 1 1/2 tablespoons chopped fresh parsley

1. Spray a large pot with cooking spray. Add oil and heat over moderately low heat. Add onion and cook, stirring, til soft, about 5 minutes. Increase heat to moderately high. Add mushrooms and cook, stirring, until lightly browned, about 5 minutes. Add garlic and stir to blend, about 1 minute.
2. Add lentils, salt, and water to the pot. Raise heat to high and bring to a boil. Reduce heat; simmer, partially covered, stirring occasionally, until lentils are tender, 30-45 minutes.
3. Stir turkey, pepper, soy sauce, and 1/4 cup parsley into the soup. Top each serving with some of the remaining parsley.

What's great about this recipe ?			
"Easy-Fix"	✔	"Bone Health"	✔
"Quick-Fix"		"Heart Health"	✔
"Easy-Chew"	✔	"Sweetie"	
"Hands-on"		"High Fiber"	✔

SuperSource: Vits. B1, B2, B3, B6, folate, pant.acid, potassium, iron, phosphorus, zinc, copper, manganese, chromium, fiber

Nutrition information per serving: 315 calories, 35 g carbohydrates, 28 g protein, 8 g fat, 1g saturated fat, 35 mg cholesterol, 473 mg sodium, 16 g fiber. Good source of vit. C, magnesium, selenium.

Hearty Alaska Cod Chowder

Servings: 6

Fish is easy to chew, and a good source of B12 and heart-healthful fat. The microwave makes it a "quick-to-fix" dish. Reprinted courtesy of the Alaska Seafood Marketing Institute.

1 pound cod fillets, thawed if necessary
1 cup onion, chopped 1/2"
1 cup zucchini, chopped 1/2"
1 clove garlic, minced
2 tablespoons peanut or safflower oil
1 15-ounce can reduced-sodium tomatoes, chopped

2 cups reduced-sodium tomato juice
1/3 cup dry white wine or water
3/4 teaspoon salt
3/4 teaspoon basil, crushed
1/4 teaspoon bottled hot pepper sauce

1. Cut cod into 1" chunks.
2. Combine onion, zucchini, garlic and oil in 3-1/2 quart microwave proof dish. Microwave, covered, at high 4 minutes or until onion is tender. Add tomatoes, tomato juice, wine and seasonings. Microwave, covered, at high 4 minutes or until boiling. Add cod. Microwave, covered, at high 4 minutes; stir. Microwave covered, at high 4 to 6 minutes longer or until cod flakes easily when tested with a fork.

What's great about this recipe ?			
"Easy-Fix"	✔	"Bone Health"	✔
"Quick-Fix"	✔	"Heart Health"	✔
"Easy-Chew"	✔	"Sweetie"	
"Hands-on"		"High Fiber"	

SuperSource: Vit. B12, C, potassium, phosphorus, manganese, selenium, chromium

Nutrition information per serving: 157 calories, 11 g carbohydrates, 15 g protein, 5 g fat, 1 g saturated fat, 33 mg cholesterol, 349 mg sodium, 2 g fiber. Good source of vits. A, B1, B3, B6, E, K, pant.acid, iron, magnesium, copper.

Manhattan Clam and Potato Chowder

Servings: 4

An easy, microwave chowder. Clams are mineral-rich, and also a good source of B12. Reprinted courtesy of The Idaho Potato Commission.

2 large baking potatoes, with peel, diced
1/4 cup thinly sliced celery
1 medium carrot, scrubbed and chopped
1 small onion, chopped
1/2 teaspoon dried whole thyme

1 (8 ounce) bottle clam juice
1 (14 1/2-ounce) can reduced-sodium tomatoes, undrained, chopped
1 (6 1/2-ounce) can minced clams, undrained

1. Combine potatoes, celery, carrot, onion, thyme, clam juice and tomatoes in a deep 3-quart microwave-safe casserole dish; cover with microwaveable plastic wrap and microwave at HIGH 15 to 18 minutes, or until potatoes are tender, stirring every 5 minutes.
2. Stir in clams; cover and microwave at HIGH 2 to 3 minutes, or until thoroughly heated.

What's great about this recipe ?

"Easy-Fix"	✔	"Bone Health"	✔
"Quick-Fix"	✔	"Heart Health"	✔
"Easy-Chew"	✔	"Sweetie"	
"Hands-on"		"High Fiber"	✔

SuperSource: Vits. A, B3, B6, B12, C, K, potassium, iron, phosphorus, copper, manganese, selenium, chromium, fiber

Nutrition information per serving: 216 calories, 36 g carbohydrates, 16 g protein, 1 g fat, 0 g saturated fat, 33 mg cholesterol, 352 mg sodium, 4 g fiber. Good source of vits. B1, B2, E, folate, pant.acid, biotin, magnesium, zinc.

Shrimp-and-Vegetable Chowder

Servings: 6

Try frozen raw prepared shrimp; chop them 1/4" if chewing is a problem. If you use levodopa, and the protein in cow's milk blocks absorption, try soy milk instead (it will not be as rich, however).

3 tablespoons olive oil
8 ounces medium shrimp, peeled and deveined
1 onion, chopped
1/4 teaspoon cayenne
1/2 teaspoon paprika
1/2 teaspoon turmeric
1 teaspoon salt
1 pound winter squash, peeled, seeded and cut into 1-inch cubes

1 pound green cabbage (about 1/2 a small head), chopped
1 pound red potatoes, cut in 1-inch cubes
2 cups frozen corn kernels or 1 (15 ounce) can corn
2 quarts water
1 cup evaporated skim milk
1 cup frozen peas (optional)

1. In a large pot, heat the oil over moderate heat. Add the shrimp and cook, stirring, until the shrimp are pink and firm, about 3-5 minutes. Remove with a slotted spoon and set aside.
2. Add the onion, cayenne, paprika, turmeric, and salt to pot. Cook, stirring, until the onion is translucent, about 5 minutes. Add squash, cabbage, potatoes, corn, and water; cover and bring to a boil. Reduce the heat and simmer, partly covered, until potatoes are tender, about 15 minutes.
3. Add milk and simmer 10 minutes. Stir in shrimp and peas. Cook until the shrimp and peas are just heated through, about 2-3 minutes.

What's great about this recipe ?			
"Easy-Fix"		"Bone Health"	✔
"Quick-Fix"		"Heart Health"	✔
"Easy-Chew"	✔	"Sweetie"	
"Hands-on"		"High Fiber"	✔

SuperSource: Vits. A, B1, B3, B6, B12, C, K, folate, pant.acid, potassium, iron, phosphorus, copper, manganese, selenium, chromium, fiber

Nutrition information per serving: 309 calories, 54 g carbohydrates, 19 g protein, 4 g fat, 1 g saturated fat, 75 mg cholesterol, 332 mg sodium, 8 g fiber. Good source of vit. B2, calcium, magnesium, zinc.

Salmon and White Bean Stew

Servings: 6

Salmon offers omega-3 fatty acids, beans have folate and fiber. What a great stew! Reprinted courtesy of Alaska Seafood Marketing Institute.

1 tablespoon olive oil
4 cloves garlic, minced
1 medium onion, chopped
1 teaspoon oregano
2 cups chopped zucchini
2 carrots, scrubbed and chopped
1 tablespoon Worcestershire sauce
2 (15-ounce) cans small white beans, with liquid

1/2 cup dry sherry or chicken broth
Pepper, to taste
1 (7.5 ounce) can Alaska salmon, including bones, drained and flaked, bones mashed
1/2 cup loosely packed chopped fresh basil
1 cup tomato, diced

1. Heat oil in a sauté pan; add the garlic, onion and oregano and sauté until the onion is translucent. Add the zucchini, carrot and Worcestershire sauce; stir and sauté for 3 to 4 minutes.
2. Drain beans, saving liquid. Add the beans to the sauté along with the bean liquid and enough water to equal a total of 4 cups of liquid. Add the sherry and pepper. Bring to a boil; reduce to simmer and cook 5 minutes. Add the salmon, basil and diced tomato. Cook 3 to 4 minutes until salmon is heated through. Ladle into 4 warm serving bowls, and serve at once.

What's great about this recipe ?			
"Easy-Fix"	✔	"Bone Health"	✔
"Quick-Fix"	✔	"Heart Health"	✔
"Easy-Chew"	✔	"Sweetie"	
"Hands-on"		"High Fiber"	✔

SuperSource: Vits. A, B6, B12, D, potassium, iron, phosphorus, copper, selenium, chromium, fiber

Nutrition information per serving: 252 calories, 32 g carbohydrates, 17 g protein, 5 g fat, 1 g saturated fat, 20 mg cholesterol, 353 mg sodium, 9 g fiber. Good source of vits. B1, B2, B3, C, folate, pant.acid, biotin, zinc, manganese.

Golden Shrimp Chowder

Serving: 4

Use bottled minced garlic and frozen prepared shrimp for easy, quick preparation.* If chewing is a concern, chop the shrimp to 1/4" pieces.*

1 1/2 pounds boiling potatoes, unpeeled, cut in 1" chunks
2 cups chicken broth
1/2 teaspoon turmeric
2 tablespoons olive oil
3 tablespoons minced garlic
8 ounces uncooked shrimp, peeled, deveined
1/4 teaspoon crushed hot red pepper flakes

1 medium tomato, diced, or 8 oz canned tomatoes with juice, chopped
1 (10-ounce) package frozen peas, thawed
1/2 teaspoon dried basil
2 tablespoons minced parsley, or 1 teaspoon dried parsley

1. Cook potatoes in large saucepan of boiling water until just tender. Drain. Whisk broth and turmeric together in small bowl.

2. Heat oil in heavy large skillet over medium-low-heat. Add garlic and sauté until light golden, about 1 minute. Add shrimp and hot pepper; increase heat to medium-high, stirring till shrimp is evenly covered with hot oil. Add tomatoes and chicken broth. Bring to boil, stirring constantly. Cook until shrimp are just done, about 5 minutes. Transfer shrimp to bowl, using slotted spoon.

3. Add potatoes to broth and boil, reducing liquid till it thickens to sauce consistency, about 6 minutes. Return shrimp to skillet. Add peas, basil, salt and pepper; cook till heated through. Garnish with parsley and serve.

What's great about this recipe ?			
"Easy-Fix"	✔*	"Bone Health"	✔
"Quick-Fix"	✔*	"Heart Health"	✔
"Easy-Chew"	✔*	"Sweetie"	
"Hands-on"		"High Fiber"	✔

SuperSource: Vits. B1, B3, B6, B12, C, pant.acid, potassium, iron, phosphorus, copper, manganese, selenium, chromium, fiber

Nutrition information per serving: 346 calories, 47 g carbohydrates, 20 g protein, 9 g fat, 2 g saturated fat, 111 mg cholesterol, 221 mg sodium, 7 g fiber. Good source of vits. A, B2, K, folate, magnesium, zinc.

Split Pea & Barley Soup

Servings: 6

Besides everything else, this recipe has almost a whole day's worth of fiber in one serving! Chop onion, carrot, and celery in a food processor, and this will be very easy to prepare.* Can be pureed and sipped from a mug, also.** May also be made in a crockery cooker – place all ingredients in the cooker and cook on "low" about 6-8 hours.

1 pound dried split peas (about 2 ½ cups)
1/2 cup hulled barley
8 cups water
4 cups reduced-sodium chicken broth, or 4 cups water and 4 chicken bouillon cubes
1 cup chopped onion

2 carrots, diced
1 stalk celery, diced
1 large clove garlic, minced
1/4 teaspoon salt
1 tablespoon dried parsley
1/4 teaspoon dried thyme
1/4 teaspoon pepper

1. Rinse and drain the split peas and barley, then add them to a large pot with water, chicken broth, onion, carrots, celery, garlic, salt, parsley, thyme, and pepper. Bring to a boil, then reduce heat and simmer for 75 minutes or until the peas are soft and barley is tender.
2. You may leave the soup chunky. If desired, you may also puree in a blender or food processor until smooth.
3. This soup freezes very well; divide it into one-or-two-serving portions and place in freezer containers. Keeps frozen for several months.

What's great about this recipe ?

"Easy-Fix"	✔*	"Bone Health"	✔
"Quick-Fix"		"Heart Health"	✔
"Easy-Chew"	✔**	"Sweetie"	
"Hands-on"	✔**	"High Fiber"	✔

SuperSource: Vits. A, B1, folate, pant.acid, potassium, iron, magnesium, phosphorus, zinc, copper, manganese, chromium, fiber

Nutrition information per serving: 354 calories, 62 g carbohydrates, 22 g protein, 3 g fat, 1 g saturated fat, 0 mg cholesterol, 152 mg sodium, 23 g fiber. Good source of vits. B2, B3, B6, K, selenium.

Parsnip, Squash, and Carrot Soup with White Beans

Servings: 4

All the vegetables can be chopped in a food processor, starting with the garlic (or use bottled minced garlic).*

2 tablespoons olive oil
1 onion, chopped
1 pound carrots, diced 1/4"
1/2 teaspoon salt
2 cloves garlic, minced
1 zucchini, diced 1/4"
1 yellow squash, diced 1/4"
6 cups canned low-sodium chicken broth or 6 cups water and 3 chicken bouillon cubes

1 (15 ounce) can reduced-sodium tomatoes with their juice, chopped
1 pound parsnips, scrubbed, and diced 1/4"
2 (15 ounce) cans navy or Great Northern beans, drained and rinsed
1/2 cup chopped fresh parsley
1/4 teaspoon black pepper

1. In a large saucepan, heat the oil over moderate heat. Add the onion, carrots, and 1/4 teaspoon of the salt and cook, stirring occasionally, until the vegetables start to soften, about 5 minutes.

2. Add the garlic, zucchini, yellow squash, broth, tomatoes, parsnips and the remaining 1/4 teaspoon salt; bring to a simmer. Reduce the heat and simmer, partially covered, until the vegetables are tender, about 20 minutes. Stir in the beans, parsley, and pepper and heat through, about 2-3 minutes.

What's great about this recipe ?			
"Easy-Fix"	✔*	"Bone Health"	✔
"Quick-Fix"		"Heart Health"	✔
"Easy-Chew"	✔	"Sweetie"	
"Hands-on"		"High Fiber"	✔

SuperSource: Vits. A, B1, B6, C, K, folate, potassium, iron, phosphorus, copper, manganese, chromium, fiber

Nutrition information per serving: 366 calories, 61 g carbohydrates, 14 g protein, 12 g fat, 3 g saturated fat, 0 mg cholesterol, 503 mg sodium, 16 g fiber. Good source of Vits. B2, B3, E, pant.acid, biotin, calcium, magnesium, selenium.

Lentil-Tomato Stew

Servings: 4

Turmeric, ginger, and cayenne all have reputed health benefits; however, you can leave them out if you wish.

2 tablespoons olive oil
1 large onion, chopped
2 stalks celery, chopped
1/2 teaspoon ground ginger
1/2 teaspoon turmeric
1/4 teaspoon cayenne
1 teaspoon salt
1/4 teaspoon pepper
1 cup brown lentils

6 cups water
1 cup boiling potato, unpeeled, diced 1/2"
1 (15-ounce) can reduced-sodium tomatoes, chopped
1 (15-ounce) can chickpeas, drained and rinsed
1/2 cup chopped parsley
1 lemon, cut in wedges

1. In a large pot, heat olive oil over moderately low heat. Add the onion and celery and cook, stirring occasionally, until the vegetables soften, about 10 minutes. Stir in the ginger, turmeric, cayenne, salt, pepper, and lentils and cook 1 minute.
2. Add the water, potato, and tomatoes to the pot. Raise heat to high and bring to a boil. Reduce the heat and simmer, partly covered, stirring occasionally, until the lentils are tender, 25 to 30 minutes. Add the chickpeas and simmer 5 minutes longer. Sprinkle with the parsley, and serve with lemon wedges.

What's great about this recipe ?

"Easy-Fix"	✔	"Bone Health"	✔
"Quick-Fix"		"Heart Health"	✔
"Easy-Chew"	✔	"Sweetie"	
"Hands-on"		"High Fiber"	✔

SuperSource: Vits. B1, B6, C, folate, pant.acid, potassium, iron, magnesium, phosphorus, zinc, copper, manganese, chromium, fiber

Nutrition information per serving: 450 calories, 77 g carbohydrates, 22 g protein, 9 g fat, 1 g saturated fat, 0 mg cholesterol, 356 mg sodium, 24 g fiber. Good source of vits. A, B2, B3, E, K.

Split-Pea Soup
Servings: 6

This is a good, basic split pea soup; and it works equally well with lentils, either red or brown. A food processor will quickly do all the chopping for you;* and if you like you can put everything into a crockery cooker and let it simmer all day – it will smell heavenly! Add the sunflower oil toward the end – it's rich in vitamin E, but too much heat will destroy it. You could, if you wish, add a 10-ounce box of frozen chopped spinach (thawed) during the last 10 minutes of cooking. It will add to the antioxidant content.

1 pound split peas (about 2 1/2 cups), rinsed well and drained
1 large onion, chopped
2 carrots, chopped
2 stalks celery, chopped
1 bay leaf
1 tablespoon dried parsley

1 teaspoon dried oregano
1 teaspoon dried basil
1 teaspoon salt
1/2 teaspoon turmeric
1/2 teaspoon ground black pepper
9-10 cups water, more if needed
2 tablespoons sunflower oil

1. Place split peas, onion, carrot, celery, bay leaf, parsley, oregano, basil, salt, turmeric, and water in a large pot and bring to a boil over high heat. Reduce heat to low and simmer till peas are tender, about 45-60 minutes, checking occasionally to see if it needs extra water. Add sunflower oil during last 5 minutes of cooking. Remove bay leaf before serving.

What's great about this recipe ?

"Easy-Fix"	✔*	"Bone Health"	✔
"Quick-Fix"		"Heart Health"	✔
"Easy-Chew"	✔	"Sweetie"	
"Hands-on"		"High Fiber"	✔

SuperSource: Vits. A, B1, E, folate, pant.acid, potassium, iron, phosphorus, copper, manganese, chromium, fiber

Nutrition information per serving: 341 calories, 51 g carbohydrates, 19 g protein, 8 g fat, 1 g saturated fat, 0 mg cholesterol, 420 mg sodium, 21 g fiber. Good source of vits. B2, B3, B6, K, magnesium, zinc.

Bean-Butternut-Corn Stew

Servings: 4

Peeling the squash takes time, but everything else is easy – bottled minced garlic, canned tomatoes, broth, beans and corn.

2 tablespoons olive oil
2 onions, chopped
1 tablespoon minced garlic
1/2 teaspoon turmeric
1/4 teaspoon cayenne
1 teaspoon dried oregano
1 (15-ounce) can reduced sodium tomatoes, chopped, with their juices

2 pounds butternut squash, peeled, seeded, cut in 1-inch chunks
1 1/2 cups reduced-sodium chicken broth or water
1/2 teaspoon salt
1 (15 ounce) can kidney beans, drained and rinsed
2 cups frozen corn kernels, or 1 (15 ounce) can corn kernels

1. In a large pot, heat olive oil over moderately low heat. Add the onions and cook, stirring occasionally, until translucent, about 5 minutes. Add the garlic, turmeric, cayenne, and oregano and cook, stirring, 1 minute.
2. Stir in chopped tomatoes, squash, broth or water, and salt and bring to a simmer. Cook, covered, stirring occasionally, until the squash is almost tender, about 15 minutes. Uncover and simmer until liquid is reduced, about 5 minutes. Add the beans and corn and cook until the corn is just tender, about 5 minutes. Serve immediately.

What's great about this recipe ?

"Easy-Fix"	✔	"Bone Health"	✔
"Quick-Fix"		"Heart Health"	✔
"Easy-Chew"	✔	"Sweetie"	
"Hands-on"		"High Fiber"	✔

SuperSource: Vits. A, B1, B3, B6, C, K, folate, pant.acid, potassium, iron, magnesium, phosphorus, copper, manganese, chromium, fiber.

Nutrition information per serving: 379 calories, 69 g carbohydrates, 13 g protein, 9 g fat, 1 g saturated fat, 0 mg cholesterol, 363 mg sodium, 17 g fiber. Good source of vits. B2, E, biotin, calcium, zinc, selenium.

Potato, Kale, and Chickpea Soup

Servings: 4

You can substitute a 10-ounce package of frozen chopped kale if you wish. You can substitute red or white "boiling potatoes" also, but they may not brown as nicely. Leave the skins on, though – they add color and contrast, besides fiber and vitamins.

1 pound kale, stems cut out, washed, chopped 1"
2 tablespoons olive oil
1 1/2 pounds russet or Yukon Gold potatoes, unpeeled and diced 1/2"
1 onion, chopped

2 cloves garlic, minced
1/2 teaspoon turmeric
1 (19 ounce) can chickpeas, drained and rinsed
2 (15 ounce) cans low-sodium chicken broth

1. In a medium saucepan, bring a quart of water to a boil. Add the kale and cook for 3 minutes. Drain; set aside.
2. In a large pot, heat the oil over moderate heat. Add the potatoes and onion and sauté, stirring frequently, until the potatoes start to brown, about 5 minutes. Add the garlic and turmeric and cook, stirring, until fragrant, about 1 minute.
3. Add the cooked kale, chickpeas, and chicken broth. Bring to a simmer and cook until the potatoes are tender, about 15 minutes.

What's great about this recipe ?			
"Easy-Fix"		"Bone Health"	✔
"Quick-Fix"		"Heart Health"	✔
"Easy-Chew"	✔	"Sweetie"	
"Hands-on"		"High Fiber"	✔

SuperSource: Vits. A, B1, B6, C, K, folate, pant.acid, potassium, iron, magnesium, phosphorus, copper, manganese, chromium, fiber

Nutrition information per serving: 485 calories, 84 g carbohydrates, 15 g protein, 11 g fat, 2 g saturated fat, 0 mg cholesterol, 470 mg sodium, 13 g fiber. Good source of vits. B2, B3, E, calcium, zinc.

Tuscan Bean Soup

Servings: 6

Canned goods are a real help here. Just chop the onion, celery, and garlic in a food processor, and use your cooked, frozen barley (see "Side Dishes")

1 cup chopped onion
1/2 cup chopped celery
3 garlic cloves, minced
1 tablespoon olive oil
3/4 teaspoon dried basil
1/4 teaspoon dried thyme
1 bay leaf
1/4 teaspoon pepper
4 cans (8 cups) reduced-sodium chicken broth
1 (15 ounce) can baby lima beans, drained and rinsed

1 (15 ounce) can garbanzo beans, drained and rinsed
1 (15 ounce) kidney beans, drained and rinsed
2 tablespoons tomato paste
1 1/2 cups cooked barley
1 large boiling potato, diced 1/2"
1 cup carrots, diced 1/2"
1 cup (lightly packed) spinach leaves, shredded 1/2"
2 tablespoons sunflower oil

1. Saute onion, celery and garlic in oil in large saucepan 2 - 3 minutes; stir in basil, thyme, bay leaf, and pepper and saute til onions are tender, 2 - 3 minutes longer.
2. Add chicken broth, all beans, and tomato paste. Bring to boil over high heat. Reduce heat to low; add cooked barley, potato, carrots and spinach and simmer uncovered, 20-25 minutes. Before serving, stir in sunflower oil; remove and discard bay leaf.

What's great about this recipe ?

"Easy-Fix"	✔	"Bone Health"	✔
"Quick-Fix"		"Heart Health"	✔
"Easy-Chew"	✔	"Sweetie"	
"Hands-on"		"High Fiber"	✔

SuperSource: Vits. A, B3, B6, C, E, potassium, iron, phosphorus, copper, manganese, selenium, chromium, fiber

Nutrition information per serving: 398 calories, 61 g carbohydrates, 17 g protein, 11 g fat, 2 g saturated fat, 5 mg cholesterol, 456 mg sodium, 13 g fiber. Good source of vits. B1, B2, K, folate, pant.acid, magnesium, zinc.

Tortellini Soup

Servings: 4

Be sure to add the sunflower oil at the end; it's a rich source of vitamin E, too much heat will destroy some of the vitamin E content.

8 ounces fresh or frozen cheese tortellini
1 tablespoon olive oil
1 tablespoon minced garlic
1/2 cup chopped onion
1/2 cup shredded carrot
1/2 cup chopped zucchini
1 cup sliced mushrooms
1 cup diced tomatoes

1 teaspoon dried basil
1 teaspoon dried thyme
2 (15 ounce) cans reduced-sodium chicken stock
3 cups spinach, washed and shredded, lightly packed
1/4 teaspoon pepper
1 tablespoon sunflower oil

1. In large saucepan, cook tortellini according to package directions. Drain and rinse. Set aside.
2. Add olive oil to same saucepan, heat to medium; saute garlic, onion, carrot, zucchini, mushrooms, tomatoes, basil, and thyme, til vegetables are soft, about 6-8 minutes.
3. Add chicken stock, and heat to simmer, about 5 minutes.
4. Add tortellini and spinach. Bring to boil, add salt and pepper. Heat 2 minutes or til spinach is wilted; stir in sunflower oil. Serve immediately.

What's great about this recipe ?			
"Easy-Fix"	✔	"Bone Health"	✔
"Quick-Fix"	✔	"Heart Health"	✔
"Easy-Chew"	✔	"Sweetie"	
"Hands-on"		"High Fiber"	✔

SuperSource: Vits. A, C, K, folate, iron, chromium

Nutrition information per serving: 302 calories, 35 g carbohydrates, 13 g protein, 13 g fat, 3 g saturated fat, 30 mg cholesterol, 300 mg sodium, 5 g fiber. Good source of vits. B2, B6, E, pant.acid, biotin, potassium, calcium, magnesium, phosphorus, copper, manganese.

Quinoa Chowder
Servings: 6

A savory, colorful soup that uses a quick-cooking, healthful grain. If chewing is a problem, add all the green onions with the cooking liquid and quinoa in Step 3.*

8 cups reduced-sodium chicken broth
3/4 cup uncooked quinoa, rinsed several times
1 tablespoon olive oil
1 garlic clove, minced
1/4 cup onion, finely chopped
1/2 teaspoon turmeric
2 cups diced baking potato, unpeeled
1 cup chopped carrot
1/4 teaspoon cayenne
1/4 tsp black pepper
3/4 cup green onions, sliced; divided
3 cups spinach, washed, stemmed, and chopped
1 tablespoon sunflower oil
3/4 cup (3 oz) shredded Cheddar cheese
1/2 cup fresh cilantro, minced

1. Combine broth and quinoa in a large pot; bring to a boil. Cover, reduce heat, and simmer 15 minutes. Remove from heat. Place sieve over a large bowl, and drain quinoa, saving the cooking liquid in the bowl; add enough water to cooking liquid to measure 6 cups. Set quinoa aside.
2. In same large pot, heat oil over medium heat. Add garlic, onion, and turmeric; cook 30 seconds. Stir in potato, carrot, cayenne, and black pepper; cook 5 minutes, stirring frequently.
3. Stir in 6 cups cooking liquid, quinoa, and 1/2 cup green onions; bring to a boil. Reduce heat, and simmer 10 minutes or til potato is tender. Stir in 1/4 cup green onions and spinach; cook 3 minutes. Stir in sunflower oil. Remove from heat. Stir in cheese and cilantro.

What's great about this recipe ?

"Easy-Fix"		"Bone Health"	✔
"Quick-Fix"		"Heart Health"	✔
"Easy-Chew"	✔*	"Sweetie"	
"Hands-on"		"High Fiber"	

SuperSource: Vits. A, K, iron, phosphorus, copper, manganese, chromium

Nutrition information per serving: 294 calories, 32 g carbohydrates, 12 g protein, 14 g fat, 5 g saturated fat, 15 mg cholesterol, 279 mg sodium, 4 g fiber. Good source of vits. B1, B2, B3, B6, C, E, folate, pant.acid, biotin, potassium, calcium, magnesium, zinc, fiber.

Autumn Pumpkin Soup

Servings: 4

It takes time to peel the pumpkin (or better yet, butternut squash!) but it's worth it. Roasting the pumpkin before simmering caramelizes the outside, and gives a deeper, richer, and sweeter flavor. The pureed soup may be sipped from a mug – omit the pine nuts, though; also omit if chewing is difficult.* (Hint: it's much easier to cut up 2-3 small squash than 1 large one!)

4 cups pumpkin, or butternut squash, peeled and cut in 2"-3" chunks (about 1 1/2 pounds)
1 onion, peeled, cut in wedges
1 tablespoon olive oil
1 (15 ounce) can reduced-sodium chicken broth

1/4 teaspoon salt
1 teaspoon minced garlic
1/2 teaspoon turmeric
1/2 cup yogurt for garnish
1/2 cup minced parsley, for garnish
4 tablespoons toasted pine nuts for garnish

1. Cut pumpkin or squash into several large pieces, then cut in 2-3" chunks. Remove seeds and strings, then cut in smaller chunks and peel.
2. In large heavy pan (preferably cast-iron) over medium-high heat, roast squash or pumpkin chunks and onion wedges in oil, til caramelized (dark brown) on all sides -- 10 minutes or so. Transfer to a large pot, add broth plus enough water to cover, salt, garlic, and turmeric. Bring to boil over high heat, then reduce heat to low and simmer 20 minutes til cooked through.
3. Puree in blender. Reheat. Place in tureen, garnish with the yogurt and parsley and scatter toasted pine nuts over all.

What's great about this recipe ?			
"Easy-Fix"		"Bone Health"	✔
"Quick-Fix"		"Heart Health"	✔
"Easy-Chew"	✔*	"Sweetie"	
"Hands-on"	✔*	"High Fiber"	

SuperSource: Vit. A, C, iron, copper, manganese, chromium

Nutrition information per serving: 166 calories, 16 g carbohydrates, 7 g protein, 9 g fat, 2 g saturated fat, 2 mg cholesterol, 224 mg sodium, 2 g fiber. Good source of vits. B1, B2, B3, folate, pant.acid, E, potassium, magnesium, phosphorus, zinc.

Green Pea Soup

6 servings

Fresh green peas make a beautiful, elegant, and refreshing soup – quite different from split pea soup. If you cannot tolerate milk, try one of the soy or rice milk substitutes. Can be sipped from a mug.*

4 cups shelled fresh peas or 20 ounces frozen peas
1/2 cup coarsely chopped leeks
1/2 cup water or chicken broth
2 sprigs mint (optional)
1 teaspoon salt
1/2 teaspoon dried basil, crumbled

1/2 teaspoon marjoram, crumbled
1/4 teaspoon thyme
1/4 teaspoon pepper
1 tablespoon sugar (optional)
1 1/2 quarts skim milk, room temperature
1 tablespoon sunflower oil

1. Combine peas, leeks and water or broth in medium saucepan; bring just to boiling, but do not boil. Whirl mixture, plus mint, salt, basil, marjoram, thyme, pepper, and sugar and milk in blender til smooth. Pour mixture into saucepan; heat thoroughly. Remove from heat, stir in sunflower oil. Garnish with fresh mint sprigs if desired.

What's great about this recipe ?

"Easy-Fix"	✔	"Bone Health"	✔
"Quick-Fix"	✔	"Heart Health"	✔
"Easy-Chew"	✔	"Sweetie"	
"Hands-on"	✔*	"High Fiber"	✔

SuperSource: Vits. B1, B2, B12, D, K, iron, phosphorus, chromium

Nutrition information per serving: 210 calories, 32 g carbohydrates, 14 g protein, 3 g fat, 1 g saturated fat, 4 mg cholesterol, 320 mg sodium, 6 g fiber. Good source of vits. A, B3, B6, C, E, folate, pant.acid, biotin, potassium, calcium, magnesium, zinc, copper, manganese, selenium, fiber.

Cold Soups

Gazpacho

Servings: 6

A tangy, thick, slightly spicy soup, that can be sipped from a mug if you choose.* It doesn't require garnishes, but they add a nice touch. A dollop of yogurt, a sprinkling of toasted almonds or pine nuts, or some croutons are all good choices.

3 cups coarsely chopped, cored and peeled tomatoes

1 1/2 cups peeled and coarsely chopped cucumbers

1 green pepper, cored, seeded, chopped

1 clove garlic, sliced

1/2 cup water

1 tablespoon olive oil

3 tablespoons sunflower oil

1/4 cup wine vinegar (or fresh lemon juice)

2 slices fresh whole wheat bread, cubed

1/8 teaspoon cayenne

1/2 teaspoon salt

1. Puree all ingredients in a blender. Chill at least one hour. Also, chill soup bowls or mugs ahead of time. Serve gazpacho in chilled soup bowls. Pass garnishes, if desired.

Note: Some possible garnishes – croutons, finely diced cucumber, onion, and/or green pepper. Alternatively, toasted pine nuts, sliced almonds, a spoonful of yogurt.

What's great about this recipe ?			
"Easy-Fix"	✔	"Bone Health"	
"Quick-Fix"	✔	"Heart Health"	✔
"Easy-Chew"	✔	"Sweetie"	
"Hands-on"	✔*	"High Fiber"	✔

SuperSource: Vits. C, E, chromium

Nutrition information per serving: 133 calories, 11 g carbohydrates, 2 g protein, 10 g fat, 1 g saturated fat, 0 mg cholesterol, 263 mg sodium, 3 g fiber. Good source of vits. B6, K, potassium, iron, copper.

Summertime Carrot Soup

Servings: 6

This versatile soup can be served hot, cold, or at room temperature; it can also be sipped from a mug.* It keeps, refrigerated, for two or three days.

1 1/2 pounds carrots, roughly cut in 1" chunks
1 large onion, sliced 1/2"
1 baking potato, with peel, cut in 1" chunks
1 pound tomatoes, roughly chopped
2 tablespoons green onions, green and white parts, sliced ½"
1/4 teaspoon cayenne

1/2 teaspoon turmeric
1/2 teaspoon ground ginger
1/2 teaspoon salt
3 cups chicken broth or water
2 cups skim milk
1 tablespoon sunflower oil
1/4 cup sliced almonds, toasted
1/4 cup minced parsley

1. Combine the carrots, onion, potato, tomatoes, green onions, cayenne, turmeric, ginger, salt, and broth in a large pot and bring to a boil. Lower the heat and simmer, covered, for 30 minutes, or until vegetables are soft. Working in batches, puree soup in a blender or food processor.
2. Return the soup to the pot and stir in the milk.
3. To serve hot: reheat the soup, stir in sunflower oil, and serve sprinkled with parsley and sliced almonds.
4. To serve at room temperature, stir in sunflower oil and allow to stand until it cools slightly.
5. To serve cold, stir in sunflower oil and refrigerate for at least two hours. Serve with a spoonful of yogurt.

What's great about this recipe ?

"Easy-Fix"	✔	"Bone Health"	✔
"Quick-Fix"		"Heart Health"	✔
"Easy-Chew"	✔	"Sweetie"	
"Hands-on"	✔*	"High Fiber"	✔

SuperSource: Vits. A, C, E, potassium, iron, phosphorus, copper, chromium, fiber

Nutrition information per serving: 214 calories, 32 g carbohydrates, 8 g protein, 7 g fat, 1 g saturated fat, 3 mg cholesterol, 361 mg sodium, 6 g fiber. Good source of vits. B1, B2, B3, B6, B12, K, pant.acid, biotin, magnesium, manganese.

Chilled Spinach Soup

Servings: 4

The vegetables need only rough chopping in this recipe, because they'll be pureed after cooking. Serve in mugs,* with a dusting of cayenne if you like it; or a spoonful of yogurt.

6 cups reduced-sodium chicken broth
1 onion, coarsely chopped
1 carrot, scrubbed, sliced in 1" chunks
2 stalks celery, sliced in 1" chunks
1/2 cup uncooked brown rice, rinsed
3 cups fresh spinach, washed, stemmed, and roughly chopped

1 cup washed, roughly chopped fresh parsley
1/4 teaspoon salt
1/4 teaspoon ground black pepper
1/4 teaspoon cayenne pepper
1 tablespoon sunflower oil

1. Place broth, onion, carrot, celery, and rice in large pot. Over high high, bring to a boil. Cover tightly, reduce heat to low, and simmer for 40 - 60 minutes, until rice is tender (time will depend on type of rice).
2. Add spinach and parsley to pot; simmer, stirring, until spinach is wilted and tender, about 3-5 minutes. Stir in salt, pepper, cayenne, and sunflower oil.
3. Transfer to blender or food processor in batches; blend until smooth.
4. Refrigerate overnight. May also be served warm or at room temperature.

What's great about this recipe ?			
"Easy-Fix"	✔	"Bone Health"	✔
"Quick-Fix"		"Heart Health"	✔
"Easy-Chew"	✔	"Sweetie"	
"Hands-on"	✔*	"High Fiber"	✔

SuperSource: Vit. A, C, K, folate, iron, chromium

Nutrition information per serving: 191 calories, 24 g carbohydrates, 7 g protein, 8 g fat, 2 g saturated fat, 0 mg cholesterol, 272 mg sodium, 4 g fiber. Good source of vits. B6, E, biotin, potassium, magnesium, copper, manganese.

Salads

Sweet-Potato Salad

Servings: 4

The combination of sweet potatoes with sunflower oil makes this salad an antioxidant powerhouse. Note: it is high in sodium; if you have high blood pressure, kidney disease, or congestive heart failure, you may need to cut the amount of ham in half.

2 pounds sweet potatoes (about 3 large), peeled, diced 1/2"
8 ounces smoked ham, diced 1/4"
2 tablespoons thinly-sliced green onions
1/4 cup cider vinegar

1/4 teaspoon fresh-ground black pepper
1/4 cup sunflower oil
4 cups Romaine lettuce, shredded 1/4" and chopped
1/4 cup sliced almonds, lightly toasted

1. Bring two quarts of water to a boil. Add the sweet potatoes and boil until barely tender when pierced with a fork, about 8-10 minutes. Drain and place in serving bowl. Add almonds, ham and green onions.
2. In small bowl, whisk together the vinegar, pepper and sunflower oil. Pour half the dressing into the sweet-potato mixture and toss lightly.
3. Pour remaining dressing over lettuce and toss well. Divide lettuce among 4 plates. Top with sweet potato mixture, dividing evenly among plates. Sprinkle with toasted almonds.

What's great about this recipe ?			
"Easy-Fix"	✔	"Bone Health"	✔
"Quick-Fix"	✔	"Heart Health"	✔
"Easy-Chew"		"Sweetie"	
"Hands-on"		"High Fiber"	✔

SuperSource: Vits. A, B2, B6, C, E, K, folate, pant.acid, biotin, potassium, iron, phosphorus, copper, manganese, chromium, fiber

Nutrition information per serving: 469 calories, 59 g carbohydrates, 16 g protein, 21 g fat, 3 g saturated fat, 27 mg cholesterol, 704 mg sodium, 9 g fiber. Good source of vits. B1, B3, magnesium.

Double Decker Pasta Salad

Servings: 6

A rainbow of colors in a tangy dressing. Reprinted courtesy of the National Pasta Association.

8 ounces elbow macaroni, medium shells, or other medium pasta shape, uncooked

2 cups fresh green beans, cut in half or 1 (10-ounce) package frozen green beans, thawed and drained

1 cup plain low-fat yogurt

1 tablespoon Dijon mustard

2 tablespoons honey

2 medium carrots, grated

1 red apple (about 1 1/4 cups), diced 1/2"

1 (6 1/8-ounce) can white tuna packed in water, drained

1/4 cup chopped walnuts

1/2 cup grated Cheddar cheese

1. Prepare pasta according to package directions; drain.
2. Blanch green beans by cooking in pot of boiling water for 2 minutes. Drain and rinse well with cold water. Drain again.
3. Whisk together yogurt, Dijon mustard and honey; set aside.
4. Spread half of the cooked pasta in the bottom of a 3-quart glass bowl, trifle dish or glass baking dish. Top with half each of the green beans, carrot, apple and tuna.
5. Drizzle half of the dressing evenly over salad. Repeat this procedure with the remaining half of the ingredients to create a colorful salad that can be seen through the glass dish. Sprinkle walnuts and Cheddar cheese on top.
6. Serve at room temperature, or cover and chill for 30 minutes.

What's great about this recipe ?

"Easy-Fix"	✔	"Bone Health"	✔
"Quick-Fix"	✔	"Heart Health"	✔
"Easy-Chew"		"Sweetie"	
"Hands-on"		"High Fiber"	

SuperSource: Vits. A, B1, B2, B3, B12, iron, phosphorus, selenium, chromium

Nutrition information per serving: 342 calories, 45 g carbohydrates, 18 g protein, 10 g fat, 3 g saturated fat, 68 mg cholesterol, 223 mg sodium, 4 g fiber. Good source of vits. B6, K, biotin, potassium, calcium, magnesium, zinc, copper, manganese, fiber.

Tomato and Tortellini Toss

Servings: 4

In 15 minutes you can turn a handful of convenience items into a colorful main course, accented with a generous helping of fresh tomato chunks. Serve with hot garlic bread and a fresh fruit cocktail. Reprinted courtesy of Florida Tomatoes.

3 cups fresh broccoli florets, cut bite-size

1 9-ounce package (about 2-1/2 to 3 cups) cheese tortellini

1/2 cup pesto, homemade or store-bought

2 large tomatoes, cored, quartered, and cut into bite-size chunks

1/4 teaspoon black pepper

1/4 cup crumbled feta cheese for garnish

1. In 3-quart saucepan, steam the broccoli for about 5 to 6 minutes, until it is just tender-crisp. Drain and transfer to a serving bowl.
2. In same saucepan bring 2 quarts of salted water to a boil. Add the tortellini and cook until done according to the package instructions. Drain and toss with the broccoli and pesto until thoroughly coated.
3. Add the tomatoes and toss briefly. Add pepper to taste and serve at once, garnished with the feta cheese.

What's great about this recipe ?			
"Easy-Fix"	✔	"Bone Health"	✔
"Quick-Fix"	✔	"Heart Health"	✔
"Easy-Chew"		"Sweetie"	
"Hands-on"		"High Fiber"	✔

SuperSource: Vits. A, B2, C, K, iron, chromium, fiber

Nutrition information per serving: 374 calories, 40 g carbohydrates, 19 g protein, 17 g fat, 6 g saturated fat, 58 mg cholesterol, 615 mg sodium, 7 g fiber. Good source of vits. B1, B6, B12, E, folate, pant.acid, potassium, calcium, phosphorus, copper, manganese.

Shoepeg Corn and Black Bean Salad

Servings: 6

Fast, easy, high-fiber, and tastes great, too!

1 (15 ounce) can black beans, drained
1 (15 ounce) can baby peas, drained
1 (15 ounce) can shoepeg corn, drained
3 stalks celery, chopped 1/4"
1/2 onion, chopped 1/4"
1/2 green or red bell pepper, chopped 1/2"

1 (3 ounce) jar pimientos, drained, chopped
DRESSING:
1/3 cup sugar
1/2 cup cider vinegar
1/4 cup sunflower oil
1/4 teaspoon salt
1 teaspoon paprika

1. Spoon black beans, peas, corn, celery, onion, bell pepper, and pimientos into a large bowl.
2. In small bowl, whisk together sugar, vinegar, oil, salt, and paprika.
3. Pour dressing over bean mixture. Refrigerate at least one hour. This tastes even better the next day.

What's great about this recipe ?

"Easy-Fix"	✔	"Bone Health"	✔
"Quick-Fix"	✔	"Heart Health"	✔
"Easy-Chew"		"Sweetie"	
"Hands-on"		"High Fiber"	✔

SuperSource: Vits. E, C, iron, chromium, fiber

Nutrition information per serving: 272 calories, 45 g carbohydrates, 8 g protein, 10 g fat, 1 g saturated fat, 0 mg cholesterol, 415 mg sodium, 9 g fiber. Good source of vits. A, B1, B6, K, folate, pant.acid, potassium, phosphorus, copper, manganese.

Lentil Salad with Spinach

Servings: 6

This is a wonderful way to eat spinach – it's not quite "cooked" yet it's wilted and easier to chew than raw spinach. A great summertime main-dish salad.

1 pound lentils (about 2 1/2 cups), rinsed and picked over
1 cup diced carrot
1 cup diced onion
1 clove garlic, halved
1 bay leaf
1 pound spinach, washed, stemmed, and chopped 1"

1/4 cup lemon juice, preferably freshly squeezed
1/2 teaspoon salt
1/2 teaspoon fresh-ground black pepper
1/4 cup sunflower oil
1 tomato, chopped
1/2 cup minced parsley

1. In a 3 to 4 quart pot, combine the lentils, carrot, onion, garlic, bay leaf, and enough water to cover by 2 inches. Bring to a boil. Reduce heat to low and simmer, partially covered, until the lentils are tender to the bite but not breaking apart, about 20-30 minutes. Drain and discard the garlic and bay leaf. Stir in the spinach, allowing it to wilt.
2. In small bowl, whisk together lemon juice, salt, and pepper. Slowly whisk in the sunflower oil.
3. Pour dressing over lentils and spinach. Toss lightly to mix. Add tomatoes and toss again. Sprinkle with parsley. Serve immediately, at room temperature.

What's great about this recipe ?			
"Easy-Fix"	✔	"Bone Health"	✔
"Quick-Fix"	✔	"Heart Health"	✔
"Easy-Chew"	✔	"Sweetie"	
"Hands-on"		"High Fiber"	✔

SuperSource: Vits. A, B1,B2, B6, C, E, K, folate, pant.acid, potassium, iron, magnesium, phosphorus, zinc, copper, manganese, chromium, fiber

Nutrition information per serving: 396 calories, 55 g carbohydrates, 26 g protein, 10 g fat, 1 g saturated fat, 0 mg cholesterol, 274 mg sodium, 28 g fiber. Good source of vit. B3, biotin.

Panzanella With Beans

Servings: 4   Yield: 8 cups

The toasted bread cubes soak up the wonderful dressing. I prefer sweet onions when they're available, but red onion is good too. Use your food processor for chopping vegetables and mincing garlic, this will go together quickly. You might like to add some cubed Swiss or Cheddar cheese, or a chopped hard-cooked egg.

6 tablespoons red wine vinegar
2 tablespoons sunflower oil
1/4 teaspoon salt
1/4 teaspoon black pepper
1 garlic clove, minced
2 cups chopped tomato
1 cup cucumber, peeled, seeded, diced 1/2"

1/2 cup bell pepper, diced 1/2"
1/4 cup sweet or red onion, chopped
1 (15 ounce) can white beans or garbanzo beans, drained
4 cups cubed French or Italian bread, toasted
1/2 cup parsley, chopped
2 tablespoons fresh basil, minced

1. In large serving bowl, whisk together vinegar, oil, salt, pepper, and garlic. Add tomato, cucumber, bell pepper, onion, and beans and toss to combine with dressing.
2. Marinate at room temperature for 20 minutes.
3. Add toasted bread cubes, parsley, & basil. Toss gently to coat. Serve immediately.

What's great about this recipe ?			
"Easy-Fix"	✔	"Bone Health"	✔
"Quick-Fix"	✔	"Heart Health"	✔
"Easy-Chew"		"Sweetie"	
"Hands-on"		"High Fiber"	✔

SuperSource: Vits. B1, C, E, folate, iron, phosphorus, copper, manganese, fiber

Nutrition information per serving: 335 calories, 51 g carbohydrates, 13 g protein, 10 g fat, 1 g saturated fat, 0 mg cholesterol, 398 mg sodium, 9 g fiber. Good source of vits. A, B2, B3, B6, K, pant.acid, potassium, magnesium, zinc, chromium.

Quick Cold Vegetable Salad

Servings: 6

Slice the carrots, dice the potatoes, and cook them together with the eggs in the same pot, for quick preparation and easy cleanup.* Remove the eggs after 14 minutes, the potatoes and carrots will take about 20 minutes total.

1 cup sliced carrots, cooked
1 cup reduced-sodium canned peas, drained
1 cup reduced-sodium canned green beans, drained
1 cup potatoes (with skin), diced, boiled

1 (4 ounce) can sliced mushrooms, drained
2 tablespoons sweet pickle relish
1/4 cup mayonnaise
1 (15 ounce) can reduced-sodium sliced beets
2 hard-cooked eggs, sliced

1. In large serving bowl, lightly toss together the carrots, peas, green beans, potato, mushrooms, and pickle relish. Add mayonnaise, and stir till well mixed. Arrange sliced beets and eggs around the edge of salad. Chill or serve at once.

What's great about this recipe ?

"Easy-Fix"	✔*	"Bone Health"	✔
"Quick-Fix"	✔*	"Heart Health"	✔
"Easy-Chew"	✔	"Sweetie"	
"Hands-on"		"High Fiber"	✔

> SuperSource: Vit. A, copper, chromium, fiber

Nutrition information per serving: 188 calories, 21 g carbohydrates, 5 g protein, 9 g fat, 2 g saturated fat, 77 mg cholesterol, 231 mg sodium, 4 g fiber. Good source of vits. B2, B6, C, E, K, folate, pant.acid, biotin, potassium, iron, phosphorus, manganese, selenium.

Chilled Green Bean and Red Potato Salad

Servings: 4

If chewing is a problem, mince or omit the bell pepper; substitute onion powder and garlic powder to taste.* Recipe courtesy of the Florida Department of Agriculture and Consumer Services

8 ounces green beans, snipped
1 pound small red potatoes, quartered
1/2 cup red bell pepper, diced
1/4 cup red onion, minced
1/2 teaspoon garlic, minced
1 tablespoon fresh dill (or 1/2 teaspoon dried dill)

1/2 teaspoon sugar
2 teaspoons Dijon mustard
2 tablespoons balsamic vinegar
1/4 cup sunflower oil
1/2 teaspoon salt
Freshly ground black pepper to taste

1. Cook green beans in boiling, salted water until crisp-tender, approximately 5 minutes. Remove with slotted spoon and cool with cold water. Cook potatoes in same pot and same water until fork tender, about 20 minutes. Cool and place in bowl with beans and peppers.
2. Whisk together remaining ingredients and pour over vegetables. Toss gently and refrigerate for 1 hour.

What's great about this recipe ?

"Easy-Fix"	✔	"Bone Health"	✔
"Quick-Fix"		"Heart Health"	✔
"Easy-Chew"	✔*	"Sweetie"	
"Hands-on"		"High Fiber"	✔

SuperSource: Vits. B6, C, E, iron, copper, chromium, fiber

Nutrition information per serving: 280 calories, 37 g carbohydrates, 4 g protein, 14 g fat, 1 g saturated fat, 0 mg cholesterol, 158 mg sodium, 5 g fiber. Good source of vits. B1, B2, B3, K, pant.acid, potassium, magnesium, phosphorus, manganese.

Grated Parsnip Salad

Servings: 4

The parsnips are rich in fiber, folate, and vitamin C, while carrots add vitamin A and beta-carotene. Mayonnaise binds the ingredients, making it easier to scoop onto a fork or spoon, and adds vitamin E, as does the sunflower oil. Parsley contains vitamin A, and is a mild diuretic, helpful for those with fluid retention.

2 cups shredded parsnips
1/2 cup finely chopped celery
1 cup shredded carrot
1/4 cup minced fresh parsley

1/4 cup mayonnaise
1 tablespoon sunflower oil
1 tablespoon lemon juice
1/4 teaspoon salt

1. Combine parsnip, celery, carrot, and parsley in bowl.
2. In another small bowl, whisk together mayonnaise, sunflower oil, lemon juice, and salt. Stir into parsnip mixture, tossing lightly. Serve at once or chill before serving.

What's great about this recipe ?

"Easy-Fix"	✔	"Bone Health"	
"Quick-Fix"	✔	"Heart Health"	✔
"Easy-Chew"		"Sweetie"	
"Hands-on"		"High Fiber"	✔

SuperSource: Vits. A, E, chromium, fiber

Nutrition information per serving: 202 calories, 17 g carbohydrates, 1 g protein, 15 g fat, 2 g saturated fat, 10 mg cholesterol, 252 mg sodium, 4 g fiber. Good source of vits. C, folate, pant.acid, potassium, iron, copper, manganese.

Vegetable-Potato Salad With Lime Vinaigrette

Servings: 6

If you wish, you can add a hard-cooked egg per person. Canned tuna, leftover turkey or chicken, or a handful of sunflower seeds will go very well, also! The sunflower oil provides 62% of your day's vitamin E.

2 cups red-skinned potatoes, unpeeled, diced 1/2"
2 cups carrot, diced 1/2"
2 cups cauliflower florets, about 1"
2 cups string beans, cut in 1" pieces
1 medium cucumber, peeled, seeded, and chopped 1/4"
1/4 cup sweet onion, minced

2 cups cilantro leaves, washed
1/2 cup fresh lime juice
2 large cloves garlic
6 tablespoons sunflower oil
1 tablespoon mayonnaise
1 teaspoon sugar, or to taste
1/2 teaspoon salt
1/2 teaspoon black pepper

1. Cook potatoes in boiling salted water to cover just til tender but not mushy; drain well. Transfer to a bowl and dress lightly with 1 cup Lime Vinaigrette.

2. Meanwhile, steam carrots, cauliflower and beans in steamer basket above water til crisp-tender. (Put in carrots to steam first, add cauliflower and beans after 6 minutes.) Add steamed vegetables to potatoes; add cucumber and onion, and add a little more Vinaigrette. Serve immediately, or chill briefly; add a little more Vinaigrette if necessary.

3. Lime Vinaigrette: In a blender place cilantro, lime juice and garlic, and blend til cilantro is coarsely chopped. Add oil, mayonnaise, sugar, salt and pepper, pulsing and scraping sides of blender. Makes about 1 1/2 cups.

What's great about this recipe ?

"Easy-Fix"		"Bone Health"	✔
"Quick-Fix"	✔	"Heart Health"	✔
"Easy-Chew"		"Sweetie"	
"Hands-on"		"High Fiber"	✔

SuperSource: Vits. A, E, B6, C, iron, copper, manganese, chromium, fiber

Nutrition information per serving: 277 calories, 32 g carbohydrates, 4 g protein, 16 g fat, 2 g saturated fat, 2 mg cholesterol, 257 mg sodium, 6 g fiber. Good source of vits. B1, B2, B3, K, folate, pant.acid, potassium, magnesium, phosphorus.

Sandwiches
Egg-less Egg Salad Sandwich

Servings: 4   Yield: 2 cups

If you haven't yet tried tofu, this is a great way to get started! Pack the spread firmly on slices of bread, so it won't fall off. Cut sandwiches into quarters, if necessary to make them easier to handle.

8 oz tofu, hard or firm
4 tablespoons mayonnaise
2 tablespoons pickle relish
1 tablespoon lemon juice
1/2 teaspoon minced garlic
1/8 teaspoon pepper
1/4 teaspoon dill weed

2 green onions, sliced, chopped fine
1 medium carrot, finely grated
1 celery stalk, minced fine
1/2 cup finely diced green or red bell pepper
1 hard-cooked egg, chopped
4 slices whole wheat bread

1. Drain tofu on paper towel, one hour; or squeeze as much liquid as possible out with your hands. Crumble.
2. Mix together mayonnaise, pickle, lemon juice, garlic, pepper, and dill weed thoroughly. Add tofu, green onion, carrot, celery, bell pepper, and egg to mayonnaise mixture, and blend thoroughly.
3. Spread on slices of whole-wheat bread and serve open-face.

What's great about this recipe ?

"Easy-Fix"	✔	"Bone Health"	
"Quick-Fix"	✔	"Heart Health"	✔
"Easy-Chew"		"Sweetie"	
"Hands-on"	✔	"High Fiber"	

SuperSource: Vit. A, manganese, selenium, chromium

Nutrition information per serving: 257 calories, 19 g carbohydrates, 10 g protein, 16 g fat, 3 g saturated fat, 63 mg cholesterol, 306 mg sodium, 3 g fiber. Good source of vits. B1, B2, C, E, biotin, iron, phosphorus, copper, fiber.

Scrambled Egg and Tomato Sandwich

Servings: 4

Hearty grilled bread stuffed with savory egg-tomato scramble–great any time of day! You could also serve the scrambled egg by itself, with toasted bread on the side. Reprinted courtesy of The Florida Tomato Committee.

8 slices country-style whole grain bread, 1/2-inch thick
1 tablespoon olive oil
2 tablespoon butter
2 cloves garlic, peeled and finely chopped
4 tablespoons Italian parsley, finely chopped

1/4 teaspoon hot pepper flakes
4 large eggs, lightly beaten
1 large ripe tomato, cored and finely diced
1 tablespoon capers
1/4 teaspoon freshly ground pepper
12 fresh basil leaves
1 tablespoon Parmesan cheese

1. Lightly brush the slices of bread with olive oil, then grill or broil each slice. Set aside and keep warm.
2. Place butter in a medium-size sauté pan over low heat. When the butter melts, add the garlic, parsley, hot pepper flakes, and cook for 2 to 3 minutes. Add the eggs and stir slowly over low heat until the mixture starts to form small curds (careful not to overcook). Gently fold in the tomatoes and capers, and cook briefly, to warm. Add pepper.
3. Arrange and divide the egg mixture onto the 4 slices of toasted bread. Top each with 3 basil leaves and sprinkle with Parmesan cheese. Cover with remaining 4 slices of toast and cut in half. Serve immediately.

What's great about this recipe ?

"Easy-Fix"	✔	"Bone Health"	✔
"Quick-Fix"	✔	"Heart Health"	
"Easy-Chew"	✔	"Sweetie"	
"Hands-on"	✔	"High Fiber"	✔

SuperSource: Vits. B1, B2, B3, B6, B12, K, folate, pant.acid, biotin, iron, zinc, copper, chromium, fiber

Nutrition information per serving: 314 calories, 36 g carbohydrates, 16 g protein, 16 g fat, 6 g saturated fat, 229 mg cholesterol, 449 mg sodium, 6 g fiber. Good source of vits. A, C, calcium, magnesium, phosphorus, selenium.

Tomato Mozzarella Bruschetta

Servings: 4

Besides being "finger food" bruschetta may tempt a flagging appetite – almost everyone loves these tiny open-face sandwiches. The mozzarella helps hold everything together. If slowed stomach emptying is present, try making just one serving, then 30 minutes later a second serving.

1 pound tomatoes (about 2 medium)	1 tablespoon balsamic vinegar
1 tablespoon olive oil	1/8 teaspoon ground black pepper
1/2 cup minced fresh parsley	1/2 loaf French or Italian bread
1 teaspoon minced garlic	4 ounces shredded Mozzarella cheese

1. Preheat broiler. Wash, core, and chop tomatoes.
2. In a large bowl combine tomatoes, 1 tablespoon of the olive oil, the parsley, garlic, balsamic vinegar, and black pepper; let stand at least 30 minutes.
3. Slice bread loaf in 1/2" thick slices. Toast lightly. Spoon tomato mixture on slices, dividing evenly. Top each with Mozzarella. Broil until cheese is just melted, about 3 minutes. Serve immediately.

What's great about this recipe ?

"Easy-Fix"	✔	"Bone Health"	✔
"Quick-Fix"	✔	"Heart Health"	✔
"Easy-Chew"		"Sweetie"	
"Hands-on"	✔	"High Fiber"	

SuperSource: Vits. B1, B2, C, iron, phosphorus, chromium

Nutrition information per serving: 290 calories, 37 g carbohydrates, 13 g protein, 10 g fat, 4 g saturated fat, 16 mg cholesterol, 492 mg sodium, 3 g fiber. Good source of vits. A, B3, K, folate, pant.acid, biotin, potassium, calcium, zinc, copper, manganese, fiber.

BREADS

Betty Ann Carroll's SuperBread
Servings: 16   One Serving: two slices

Mrs. Carroll submitted this recipe to *Ask the Parkinson Dietitian*, where it has been requested and re-posted frequently. She includes directions for making it with yeast, as well as with sourdough starter. It is a dense, chewy, rich-tasting bread, especially good hot from the oven!

1 - 1 1/2 cups sourdough starter
1 1/2 cups warm water
1/4 cup dry milk (nonfat)
1 egg (optional)
2-3 teaspoons salt
3 tablespoons olive or flaxseed oil
4 tablespoons sugar
1/2 cup oat bran
1/2 cup wheat bran

1/4 cup wheat germ
1/2 cup ground flax seed
1/3 cup sunflower seeds or chopped
   pecans
1 cup rolled oats
1 1/2 cups whole-wheat flour
About 2-3 cups unbleached white
   bread flour

1. After feeding your sourdough starter, divide it into 2 equal halves. Save and refrigerate one half and use the other half to make the bread. The recipe will require 1 to 1 1/2 cups starter, depending on altitude, humidity, and other factors. If you don't have a sourdough starter, this bread can also be made by dissolving 1 or 2 packets of dry yeast in 1/4 cup of warm water with a teaspoon of sugar; let it sit a few minutes until the yeast foams.
2. Put the sourdough starter (or the yeast mixture) into a large bowl. Add and mix together the following ingredients: 1 ½ cups warm water, dry milk, egg, salt, oil, sugar, oat bran, wheat bran, wheat germ, ground flax seed, sunflower seeds, rolled oats, whole wheat flour and 1 cup white flour, beating well after each addition.
3. Place the dough on a floured surface and knead for 10 minutes working in more white flour as needed. Put the dough into a large bowl and cover with plastic wrap. Let it rise in a warm place until doubled in bulk. Bread made from dough starters may take longer to rise than bread made from dry yeast.
4. Form the bread into two loaves, place in oiled 9 1/2" x 5 1/2" pans and let rise a second time. When doubled in size, bake the loaves in a 300-degree oven for 45-55 minutes or until brown. Makes 2 loaves.

What's great about this recipe ?

"Easy-Fix"		"Bone Health"	✔
"Quick-Fix"		"Heart Health"	✔
"Easy-Chew"		"Sweetie"	
"Hands-on"	✔	"High Fiber"	✔

SuperSource: Iron, manganese, fiber

Nutrition information per serving: 218 calories, 35 g carbohydrates, 8 g protein, 7 g fat, 1 g saturated fat, 13 mg cholesterol, 248mg sodium, 5 g fiber. Good source of vit. B1, B2, B3, copper, iron, magnesium, phosphorus, selenium

Early American Corn Bread

Servings: 9

Try to find whole stone-ground corn meal and whole wheat flour. These contain the germ and bran and are much more flavorful and nutritious.

Cooking spray
1 egg
1 cup buttermilk (or one cup skim milk plus 1 teaspoon cider vinegar)
2 tablespoons honey

3 tablespoons sunflower oil
2/3 cup corn meal
3/4 cup whole wheat flour
2 teaspoons baking powder
1/4 teaspoon salt

1. Preheat oven to 425 degrees F. Spray 8" x 8" baking pan with cooking spray.
2. Whisk egg until light. Add buttermilk, honey, and oil, whisking till light and well blended.
3. In separate bowl, mix together corn meal, whole wheat flour, baking powder, and salt. Spoon dry mixture into liquid mixture, beating after each addition.
4. Spoon batter into prepared baking pan. Bake about 20 minutes or until center springs back when lightly touched.

What's great about this recipe ?

"Easy-Fix"	✔	"Bone Health"	
"Quick-Fix"	✔	"Heart Health"	
"Easy-Chew"	✔	"Sweetie"	
"Hands-on"	✔	"High Fiber"	

Nutrition information per serving: 140 calories, 19 g carbohydrates, 4 g protein, 6 g fat, 1 g saturated fat, 25 mg cholesterol, 201 mg sodium, 2 g fiber. Good source of vits. E, iron, phosphorus, manganese.

Raisin Bran Muffins

Servings: 24 (1 serving = 2 muffins)

These muffins taste so good, my family eats them as fast as they come out of the oven. Yet they're high in fiber; and prunes are rich in protective antioxidants, as well as possessing a natural laxative. If constipation is a problem, consider keeping a supply of these on hand.

You can cut this recipe in half, if you wish; however, these muffins freeze very well, so if you make the full batch, you'll have a quick – and delicious! – supply, all ready to pop in the microwave for breakfast or snacks, or to carry with you wherever you go. If you only have two 12-cup muffin tins, bake one batch, quickly remove the muffins, then re-line with paper cups, and bake a second batch.

1 1/2 cups wheat bran (miller's bran)
1 cup prune juice
1 pound prunes
1 cup whole wheat flour
1 tablespoon cider vinegar
3 cups skim milk
4 cups raisin bran cereal
1 cup whole wheat flour
1 tablespoon baking soda

1 1/2 teaspoons double-acting baking powder
1/2 teaspoon salt
1 tablespoon cinnamon
1/2 cup peanut or canola oil
1 cup brown sugar
2 large eggs
1/2 cup molasses
1 teaspoon vanilla

1. Preheat oven to 450 degrees F. Line muffin tins with paper cups.
2. In small bowl, stir together wheat bran and 1 cup prune juice. Let sit.
3. Place prunes in food processor. Add 1 cup of the whole wheat flour, and process until prunes are chopped to about 1/4" pieces. Transfer to medium bowl.
4. Add cider vinegar to milk and let it sour slightly. Place raisin bran cereal in a large bowl, add soured milk, and stir well. Add prune juice-bran mixture, and chopped prunes and stir to blend.
5. In separate small bowl, stir together 1 cup whole wheat flour, baking soda, baking powder, salt, and cinnamon.
6. In large (6-quart) bowl, beat oil and brown sugar; beat in eggs, molasses, and vanilla. Add one-third of flour mixture, stir well. Add one-third of bran mixture, stir well. Continue adding by thirds, till all are well blended.
7. Place about 1/4 cup batter in each muffin cup. Bake at 450 degrees for 20 minutes, or till tops spring back when lightly touched. May be frozen.

What's great about this recipe ?

"Easy-Fix"		"Bone Health"	✔
"Quick-Fix"		"Heart Health"	✔
"Easy-Chew"	✔	"Sweetie"	✔
"Hands-on"	✔	"High Fiber"	✔

SuperSource: Iron, copper, manganese, fiber

Nutrition information per serving: 247 calories, 48 g carbohydrates, 5 g protein, 6 g fat, 1 g saturated fat, 18 mg cholesterol, 316 mg sodium, 5 g fiber. Good source of vits. B1, B2, B3, B6, B12, potassium, magnesium, phosphorus, zinc, selenium.

Whole Wheat Biscuits

Servings: 10 biscuits
Denser and heavier than white biscuits, with a richer flavor.

2 cups whole wheat flour, lightly
   spooned into measuring cup
2 1/2 teaspoons baking powder
1/2 teaspoon salt

3/4 cup buttermilk
3 tablespoons sunflower oil
1 tablespoon honey

1. Preheat oven to 500 degrees F. Spray baking sheet with cooking spray.
2. In medium mixing bowl, stir together flour, baking powder, and salt. Make a well in the center, and add buttermilk, oil, and honey. Stir, starting from the center of bowl, till ingredients are well blended.
3. Make 10 biscuits, pressing in palm of hand to rounded shape. Place on prepared baking sheet. Bake about 10 minutes, or till tops are lightly browned and biscuits spring back when lightly pressed in center.

What's great about this recipe ?

"Easy-Fix"	✔	"Bone Health"	
"Quick-Fix"	✔	"Heart Health"	✔
"Easy-Chew"	✔	"Sweetie"	
"Hands-on"	✔	"High Fiber"	✔

SuperSource: manganese

Nutrition information per serving: 131 calories, 20 g carbohydrates, 4 g protein, 5 g fat, 1 g saturated fat, 1 mg cholesterol, 237 mg sodium, 3 g fiber. Good source of vits. E, iron, phosphorus, copper.

DESSERTS AND SWEETS

Sweets are an important part of our lives, and often more so with PD. Many people who never cared for sweets will develop a craving for dessert, chocolate, and other sweet-tasting foods, sometimes before PD is diagnosed, sometimes upon beginning PD medications.

It's fine to have ice cream, chocolate and other goodies; but not to the exclusion of the foods that protect us against disease – foods rich in fibers, antioxidants, minerals, and vitamins. So this section contains sweet foods that contain a little something extra – fruit, nuts, calcium, or other healthful ingredients. That doesn't mean it's not fine to order a hot fudge sundae at your favorite restaurant – but try to eat these occasionally rather than every day.

Tip: If you crave sweets, try eating a small amount of protein-rich food instead. Some people find that the protein helps to counteract the sweet craving. Examples: a hard-cooked egg; a teaspoon of peanut butter on a small whole-grain cracker; one-half ounce of cheese.

Cran-Apple Crisp

Servings: 12

You may wish to substitute blueberries for the cranberries. If so, cut the 3/4 cup sugar to 1/4 cup and add 1 tablespoon lemon juice.

Cooking spray
1 cup whole wheat flour
8 tablespoons butter (4 ounces), cut into 4 pieces
1 cup old-fashioned rolled oats
1/2 cup brown sugar, firmly packed
6 cups peeled, cored, sliced baking apples (Jonathan, Jonagold, Cortland are good choices)

2 cups fresh cranberries, rinsed and drained; or frozen cranberries
3/4 cup sugar
6 tablespoons whole wheat flour
1 teaspoon ground cinnamon
1/4 teaspoon ground cloves
1 teaspoon vanilla
1 tablespoon butter (1/2 ounce), cut into 1/4" pieces

1. Preheat oven to 350 degrees F. Spray a 13 x 9 x 2-inch baking dish with cooking spray.
2. In food processor, pulse whole wheat flour and butter, till mixture is the texture of coarse crumbs. Place in medium bowl. Add rolled oats and brown sugar and blend well. Alternatively, use a pastry cutter to blend flour and butter in a medium bowl; then mix in the oats and brown sugar.
3. In separate large bowl, stir together sliced apples, cranberries, sugar, flour, cinnamon, cloves and vanilla. Spoon into the prepared baking dish. Dot with butter. Sprinkle oat mixture evenly over the top.
4. Bake until apples are tender, about 1 1/4 hours. Cool slightly. May be served warm or cold.

What's great about this recipe ?

"Easy-Fix"		"Bone Health"	
"Quick-Fix"		"Heart Health"	
"Easy-Chew"	✔	"Sweetie"	✔
"Hands-on"		"High Fiber"	✔

SuperSource: manganese, chromium, fiber

Nutrition information per serving: 299 calories, 52 g carbohydrates, 3 g protein, 10 g fat, 6 g saturated fat, 25 mg cholesterol, 98 mg sodium, 5 g fiber. Good source of iron, phosphorus, copper.

Honey of a Carrot Cake

Servings: 12

Honey gives a moist sweetness, the carrots provide vitamin A, walnuts are heart-healthy, and whole wheat adds fiber. What a treat! Reprinted courtesy of The National Honey Board.

Cooking spray
1/2 cup (8 ounces) butter or
    margarine, softened
1 cup honey
2 eggs
2 cups finely grated carrots
1/2 cup golden raisins
1/3 cup chopped walnuts
1/4 cup orange juice

2 teaspoons vanilla
1 cup all-purpose flour
1 cup whole wheat flour
2 teaspoons baking powder
1 1/2 teaspoons ground cinnamon
1 teaspoon baking soda
1/8 teaspoon salt
1/2 teaspoon ground ginger
1/4 teaspoon ground nutmeg

1. Preheat oven to 350 degrees F. Spray a 13 x 9 x 2" baking pan with cooking spray.
2. Cream butter in large bowl. Gradually beat in honey until light and fluffy. Add eggs, one at a time, beating well after each addition.
3. Combine carrots, raisins, nuts, orange juice and vanilla in medium bowl.
4. Combine dry ingredients in separate large bowl. Add dry ingredients to creamed mixture alternately with carrot mixture, beginning and ending with dry ingredients.
5. Pour batter into greased 13 × 9 × 2-inch pan. Bake at 350°F 35 to 45 minutes or until wooden pick inserted near center comes out clean.

What's great about this recipe ?

"Easy-Fix"		"Bone Health"	✔
"Quick-Fix"		"Heart Health"	
"Easy-Chew"	✔	"Sweetie"	✔
"Hands-on"	✔	"High Fiber"	

SuperSource: Vit. A, manganese, chromium

Nutrition information per serving: 290 calories, 46 g carbohydrates, 4 g protein, 11 g fat, 6 g saturated fat, 57 mg cholesterol, 311 mg sodium, 3 g fiber. Good source of vits. B1, B2, K, biotin, iron, phosphorus, copper, fiber.

Honey Pecan Snack Spread

Servings: 12 (1 tablespoon each)

Delicious on a slice of bread as a between-meal snack. If chewing is a problem, grind the pecans before stirring into the honey-butter mixture.*

1/4 cup honey
1/4 cup (4 ounces) butter or margarine

1/2 cup pecans, broken or coarsely chopped

1. Cream honey and butter, stir in pecans.
2. Store in refrigerator. Will keep about one week. Add one tablespoon to hot oatmeal, or spread on whole-wheat bread.

What's great about this recipe ?			
"Easy-Fix"	✔	"Bone Health"	
"Quick-Fix"	✔	"Heart Health"	
"Easy-Chew"	✔*	"Sweetie"	✔
"Hands-on"		"High Fiber"	

Nutrition information per serving: 119 calories, 7 g carbohydrates, 0 g protein, 11 g fat, 5 g saturated fat, 21 mg cholesterol, 78 mg sodium, 0 g fiber.

Almond Cocoa Butter

Servings: 16

This requires a blender or food processor, but is very easy to make. Store in the refrigerator; will keep about 1 month. Spread one tablespoon on toast, or graham crackers.* If chewing is difficult, spread on buttered whole-wheat bread or add to hot cereal for an unusual taste.** Almonds, like sunflower oil, are an excellent source of vitamin E!

2 cups raw almonds
1 tablespoon sunflower oil

1 cup powdered sugar
4 tablespoons cocoa powder

1. In large skillet, over medium-low heat, lightly roast almonds until they smell fragrant. Remove from heat.
2. Place almonds in food processor or blender with oil. Process to a coarse "buttery" consistency, stopping to scrape down the sides of the bowl occasionally.
3. Gradually add powdered sugar and cocoa, continuing to stop and scrape sides of bowl.
4. Scrape almond butter into a storage container. Store in refrigerator up to one month. Serving size: 1 tablespoon.

What's great about this recipe ?

"Easy-Fix"	✔	"Bone Health"	✔
"Quick-Fix"	✔	"Heart Health"	✔
"Easy-Chew"	✔**	"Sweetie"	✔
"Hands-on"	✔*	"High Fiber"	✔

SuperSource: Vit. E, copper, fiber

Nutrition information per serving: 126 calories, 11 g carbohydrates, 4 g protein, 8 g fat, 1 g saturated fat, 0 mg cholesterol, 1 mg sodium, 2 g fiber. Good source of vit. B2, iron, magnesium, phosphorus.

Bran Banana Bars

Servings: 12

A moist, nutty, snack, easy to prepare and easy to eat. Reprinted courtesy of Monitor Sugar.

1/2 cup all-purpose flour
1/2 cup whole wheat flour
2 tablespoons ground flax seed
1/4 cup brown sugar, packed
1/2 teaspoon baking soda
1 teaspoon baking powder
1/4 teaspoon salt

1 1/2 teaspoons cinnamon
1 cup bran flakes cereal, crushed
1 cup skim milk
2 eggs
1 carrot, shredded
1 ripe banana, mashed
1/2 cup finely chopped walnuts

1. Preheat oven to 375 degrees. Lightly grease 8 1/2" × 8 1/2" baking pan.
2. In a medium bowl, combine flours, flax seed, sugar, baking soda, baking powder, salt, cinnamon and bran flakes cereal. Mix well. In a small bowl, combine milk, eggs, carrot, banana and walnuts. Add to dry ingredients. Bake for 25-35 minutes or until brown on top. Cut into 12 bars.

What's great about this recipe ?

"Easy-Fix"	✔	"Bone Health"	
"Quick-Fix"		"Heart Health"	✔
"Easy-Chew"	✔	"Sweetie"	✔
"Hands-on"	✔	"High Fiber"	✔

SuperSource: Vit. A

Nutrition information per serving: 133 calories, 20 g carbohydrates, 4 g protein, 5 g fat, 1 g saturated fat, 36 mg cholesterol, 199 mg sodium, 2 g fiber. Good source of vits. B1, B2, B6, B12, biotin, iron, phosphorus, copper, manganese.

Honey Fig Bars

Servings: 16

Sweet but not too sweet, and fiber-rich besides! Reprinted courtesy of The National Honey Board.

1 1/4 cups honey, divided
1/2 cup butter or margarine,
    softened
1 egg
1 cup all-purpose flour
2 cups whole-wheat flour

1 teaspoon baking powder
1/2 teaspoon baking soda
1 pound dried figs
2 tablespoons lemon juice
2 teaspoons grated lemon peel

1. In medium bowl, cream 3/4 cup honey with butter until light and fluffy. Beat in egg. Add flours, baking powder and baking soda; mix until combined. Wrap dough in plastic wrap and freeze until firm (about 2 hours) or refrigerate overnight. Meanwhile, in food processor with metal blade, place remaining 1/2 cup honey, figs, lemon juice and lemon peel. Process until figs are finely chopped. Set aside.

2. When dough is well chilled, dust work surface and dough with flour. Working quickly, roll dough to 1/4-inch thick. With sharp knife, trim dough into two 12 × 3-inch rectangles. (Dough trimmings can be used to make cut-out cookies.) Spread half of fig mixture evenly down center of one rectangle. Gently fold right side of rectangle over filling, then fold left side over right so they overlap. Pinch ends to seal. Repeat with remaining rectangle and fig mixture. Carefully place logs seam-side down on greased baking sheet. Bake at 350°F for 15 minutes, until lightly browned. Remove sheet from oven; allow logs to cool 5 minutes on sheet. Transfer to wire rack; cool completely. Cut into 2-inch bars.

What's great about this recipe ?

"Easy-Fix"		"Bone Health"	✔
"Quick-Fix"		"Heart Health"	
"Easy-Chew"	✔	"Sweetie"	✔
"Hands-on"	✔	"High Fiber"	✔

SuperSource: Manganese, fiber

Nutrition information per serving: 290 calories, 57 g carbohydrates, 4 g protein, 7 g fat, 4 g saturated fat, 30 mg cholesterol, 140 mg sodium, 5 g fiber. Good source of vits. B1, B3, K, iron, phosphorus, copper, chromium.

Cinnamon Applesauce Squares

Servings: 24 squares
If chewing is a problem, omit the nuts, or finely grind them.*

1 3/4 cups whole wheat flour, lightly spooned into measuring cup
3/4 cup sugar or honey
1/2 teaspoon salt
1 teaspoon baking soda
1 teaspoon cinnamon
1/4 teaspoon nutmeg

1/4 cup ground flax seed
1 egg, lightly beaten
1 cup applesauce
1/2 cup peanut or canola oil
1/2 teaspoon vanilla
1 cup raisins
1 cup walnuts, chopped

1. Preheat oven to 375 degrees F. Grease a 15" x 10" x 1" baking pan.
2. In small mixing bowl, stir together the flour, sugar, salt, soda, cinnamon, nutmeg, and flax seed. (If using honey, add it to the wet ingredients.)
3. In medium bowl, whisk together egg, applesauce, oil, vanilla (and honey, if using). Stir in raisins and nuts. Stir in flour mixture one cup at a time, beating well after each each addition.
4. Spread batter evenly in pan. Bake till top springs back when lightly pressed, about 20 - 25 minutes. Remove from oven and cool on wire rack. Cut into 24 squares. If desired, sift 2 tablespoons powdered sugar over top before cutting.

What's great about this recipe ?

"Easy-Fix"	✔	"Bone Health"	
"Quick-Fix"		"Heart Health"	
"Easy-Chew"	✔*	"Sweetie"	✔
"Hands-on"	✔	"High Fiber"	

SuperSource: Manganese

Nutrition information per serving: 159 calories, 20 g carbohydrates, 3 g protein, 9 g fat, 1 g saturated fat, 9 mg cholesterol, 110 mg sodium, 2 g fiber. Good source of biotin, iron, copper, fiber.

Easy Apple Dessert Casserole

Servings: 6

You can substitute soy or rice milk if cow's milk blocks levodopa absorption. If chewing is difficult, chop the nuts finely.*

Cooking spray
6 tart baking apples - peeled, cored and sliced
1/2 cup honey
2 tablespoons whole wheat flour
2 tablespoons ground flaxseed
1/2 teaspoon ground cinnamon
1/4 teaspoon ground nutmeg
1/4 teaspoon ground cloves
1/2 cup raisins
1/2 cup walnut or pecan halves
1/2 cup 1% milk

1. Preheat oven to 350 degrees F. Spray a two-quart baking dish with non-stick cooking spray.
2. Place apples in a large bowl; toss with honey. In a small bowl, mix together flour, flaxseed, cinnamon, nutmeg and cloves. Toss and stir together flour mixture and apples until evenly distributed. Gently stir in in raisins and walnuts. Spoon into prepared dish. Pour milk evenly over apple mixture.
3. Bake in preheated oven for 45 to 60 minutes, or until soft and bubbly. Allow to cool slightly before serving.

What's great about this recipe ?

"Easy-Fix"	✔	"Bone Health"	✔
"Quick-Fix"		"Heart Health"	✔
"Easy-Chew"	✔*	"Sweetie"	✔
"Hands-on"		"High Fiber"	

SuperSource: Copper, manganese, chromium

Nutrition information per serving: 287 calories, 57 g carbohydrates, 4 g protein, 8 g fat, 1 g saturated fat, 1 mg cholesterol, 16 mg sodium, 4 g fiber. Good source of vit. B6, biotin, potassium, iron, magnesium, phosphorus, fiber.

Honey Lime Pears

Servings: 2

A quick and easy dessert, made simple with the microwave. Reprinted courtesy of The National Honey Board.

1/2 cup honey
1/4 cup water
1/4 cup lime juice

1/2 teaspoon grated lime peel
2 firm, ripe pears, cored, halved, pared

1. To microwave: Combine honey, water and lime juice in 2-quart microwave-safe dish; microwave at HIGH (100%) 2-1/2 to 3 minutes or until mixture boils.
2. Stir in lime peel. Add pear halves to syrup; cover with vented plastic wrap and microwave at HIGH 7 to 10 minutes or until pears are tender. Serve warm or cold with poaching liquid.

What's great about this recipe ?

"Easy-Fix"	✔	"Bone Health"	
"Quick-Fix"	✔	"Heart Health"	
"Easy-Chew"	✔	"Sweetie"	✔
"Hands-on"		"High Fiber"	

SuperSource: Copper, chromium

Nutrition information per serving: 360 calories, 96 g carbohydrates, 1 g protein, 1 g fat, 0 g saturated fat, 0 mg cholesterol, 8 mg sodium, 4 g fiber. Good source of vits. C, K, iron, fiber.

Stuffed Baked Apples

Servings: 2

The microwave makes this a fast dish to serve up, for a snack as well as a dessert. You can vary the stuffing – raisins, chopped prunes, other nuts, are all delicious. If chewing is a problem, remove the skin after baking.*

2 tart baking apples
2 tablespoons brown sugar
1 tablespoon ground flax seed
1/4 teaspoon ground cinnamon

1/4 teaspoon ground nutmeg
2 tablespoons chopped cranberries
2 tablespoons chopped walnuts
2 teaspoons butter

1. Wash and dry apples and remove the core, leaving the bottom intact.
2. In a bowl, mix the brown sugar, flax seed, cinnamon, nutmeg, cranberries, and walnuts. Pack the stuffing into the apples, packing extra stuffing on top. Place 1 teaspoon butter on top of each apple.
3. Place apples in a deep microwave-safe casserole dish, and cover. Microwave 3 to 4 minutes, or until fork-tender. Allow apples to sit about 5 minutes before serving.

What's great about this recipe ?

"Easy-Fix"	✔	"Bone Health"	
"Quick-Fix"	✔	"Heart Health"	✔
"Easy-Chew"	✔*	"Sweetie"	✔
"Hands-on"		"High Fiber"	✔

SuperSource: Chromium, fiber

Nutrition information per serving: 244 calories, 36 g carbohydrates, 2 g protein, 12 g fat, 3 g saturated fat, 11 mg cholesterol, 47 mg sodium, 4 g fiber. Good source of biotin, copper, manganese, fiber.

Blackberry Zinger

Servings: 2

A tangy, frosty, fruity shake – an excellent between-meal treat or a refreshing dessert. With frozen berries available year-round, you can make this anytime of the year. Reprinted courtesy of Oregon Raspberry & Blackberry Commission.

2 cups blackberries, fresh or frozen
1/4 cup sugar
1/2 cup calcium-fortified orange juice
2 cups frozen lowfat yogurt or vanilla ice cream

1 cup crushed ice
Whole berries for garnish
Fresh mint leaves, for garnish (optional)

1. Crush/purée berries and strain through a fine sieve to yield approximately 2 cups purée. (If berries are frozen, partially thaw before crushing.)
2. Combine purée with remaining ingredients, blend until smooth and pour into chilled glasses.
3. Garnish with 2-3 berries, and fresh mint leaves if desired.

What's great about this recipe ?

"Easy-Fix"	✔	"Bone Health"	
"Quick-Fix"	✔	"Heart Health"	✔
"Easy-Chew"	✔	"Sweetie"	✔
"Hands-on"	✔	"High Fiber"	✔

SuperSource: Manganese, fiber

Nutrition information per serving: 421 calories, 89 g carbohydrates, 8 g protein, 6 g fat, 3 g saturated fat, 20 mg cholesterol, 62 mg sodium, 8 g fiber. Good source of vitamins B3, folate, C, potassium, iron, calcium, copper.

Blue Witch's Brew

Servings: 2   Yield: 2 cups

A purple-blue dessert shake – what could be more enticing?
Researchers think blueberries may help prevent oxidative damage in the
brain; time will tell, but in the meantime, we can enjoy them regardless.
Reprinted courtesy of the North American Blueberry Council.

1 1/4 cups fresh or frozen, thawed   1/2 cup lowfat frozen vanilla yogurt
     blueberries   2 tablespoons skim milk
2/3 cup apple juice   1/2 teaspoon ground cinnamon

1. In a blender whirl blueberries, apple juice, frozen yogurt, milk and
   cinnamon until smooth. Serve immediately.

What's great about this recipe ?

"Easy-Fix"	✔	"Bone Health"	
"Quick-Fix"	✔	"Heart Health"	
"Easy-Chew"	✔	"Sweetie"	✔
"Hands-on"	✔	"High Fiber"	✔

Nutrition information per serving: 143 calories, 31 g carbohydrates, 3 g protein, 2 g fat, 1 g saturated fat, 5 mg cholesterol, 31 mg sodium, 3 g fiber. Good source of vitamin C, manganese, fiber.

Honey Berry Milkshakes

Servings: 2   Yield: 2 Cups

Strawberries are rich in vitamins A and C, fiber, and antioxidants. Honey is another source of antioxidants, which makes this shake a powerful tool for health! Reprinted courtesy of The National Honey Board.

1 cup nonfat vanilla frozen yogurt
   or nonfat vanilla ice cream
1 1/4 cups strawberries

1/4 cup nonfat milk
2 tablespoons honey
2 small mint sprigs (optional)

1. Combine all ingredients except mint sprigs in blender or food processor; process about 30 seconds or until smooth.
2. Pour into tall glasses. Garnish with mint sprigs.

What's great about this recipe ?

"Easy-Fix"	✔	"Bone Health"	
"Quick-Fix"	✔	"Heart Health"	
"Easy-Chew"	✔	"Sweetie"	✔
"Hands-on"	✔	"High Fiber"	

SuperSource: Vitamin C

Nutrition information per serving: 202 calories, 42 g carbohydrates, 5 g protein, 3 g fat, 2 g saturated fat, 11 mg cholesterol, 48 mg sodium, 2 g fiber. Good source of vitamin K, calcium, manganese.

Honey-Drenched Banana with Pistachios

Servings: 4

These are a delicious dessert or between-meal snack. If chewing is a problem, you can mash the banana, drizzle w/honey, and omit or finely grind the pistachios.*

4 bananas, peeled
1/2 cup honey

1/2 cup chopped pistachios

1. Slice the bananas diagonally onto four plates. Drizzle with honey and sprinkle the pistachios over the top.

What's great about this recipe ?

"Easy-Fix"	✔	"Bone Health"	✔
"Quick-Fix"	✔	"Heart Health"	✔
"Easy-Chew"	✔*	"Sweetie"	✔
"Hands-on"		"High Fiber"	✔

SuperSource: Vits. B6, potassium, copper, fiber

Nutrition information per serving: 397 calories, 78 g carbohydrates, 5 g protein, 9 g fat, 1 g saturated fat, 0 mg cholesterol, 4 mg sodium, 7 g fiber. Good source of vits. B1, B2, C, pant.acid, iron, magnesium, phosphorus, manganese.

Strawberries a la Creme

Servings: 4

You can substitute a liqueur, such as Amaretto or Cointreau, for the orange juice, if you wish. If chewing is difficult, finely chop or grind the nuts.*

1/2 cup plain yogurt
2 tablespoons powdered sugar
1/4 teaspoon ground cinnamon
1/2 teaspoon vanilla extract
2 tablespoons orange juice

2 cups sliced fresh strawberries, washed, hulled, and cut in bite-sized pieces
2 tablespoons pecan pieces, lightly toasted

1. In a small bowl, whisk yogurt, powdered sugar, cinnamon, vanilla, and orange juice until fully mixed. Refrigerate for at least 1 hour to make the sauce slightly firm.
2. Divide berries evenly into four dessert dishes. Spoon 1/4 cup sauce over each serving. Top with nuts and serve immediately.

What's great about this recipe ?

"Easy-Fix"	✔	"Bone Health"	
"Quick-Fix"	✔	"Heart Health"	
"Easy-Chew"	✔*	"Sweetie"	✔
"Hands-on"		"High Fiber"	

SuperSource: Vit. C

Nutrition information per serving: 181 calories, 31 g carbohydrates, 2 g protein, 7 g fat, 3 g saturated fat, 11 mg cholesterol, 14 mg sodium, 2 g fiber. Good source of iron.

Stuffed Figs and Dates

Servings: 15   Serving: 1 fig and 1 date

These little confections are almost like candy, but refreshingly different. You can use low-fat or fat-free cream cheese, to lower the fat content, if you prefer. The dates are easier to chew than the figs, if that is of concern.* If chewing is not a problem, you might wish to stuff some extras with a whole toasted macadamia nut, almond, or pecan half, for variety.

15 dried figs   3 tablespoons honey
15 dates   1/4 cup pecans, finely ground
8 ounces cream cheese, softened   1/4 teaspoon cinnamon
1/2 teaspoon vanilla

1. Cut the dried stem off each fig. Slice fig from top almost to the bottom, but not quite. Slice again from top down, in an "X" and spread the fig open to contain the filling.
2. In each date, make an incision along one long side, and spread it open.
3. Beat together the cream cheese, vanilla, and honey until smooth and well blended. Beat in the nuts till evenly mixed. Spoon some filling into each fig and date.
4. Refrigerate the fruits until ready to serve.

What's great about this recipe ?			
"Easy-Fix"	✔	"Bone Health"	
"Quick-Fix"	✔	"Heart Health"	
"Easy-Chew"	✔ *	"Sweetie"	✔
"Hands-on"	✔	"High Fiber"	✔

Nutrition information per serving: 139 calories, 20 g carbohydrates, 2 g protein, 7 g fat, 3 g saturated fat, 17 mg cholesterol, 45 mg sodium, 3 g fiber.

MENUS

To help those with special concerns, I've put together some sample one-day menus from the recipes listed in this book. These are designed to provide help for some of the major concerns in PD.

> Each recipe provides about 2000-2200 calories per day; amounts will need to be adjusted to suit your individual needs.

- EASY FIX: doesn't require extensive preparation; may require use of food processor, or pre-cooked, frozen ingredients
- QUICK FIX: recipe can be prepared in about 45 minutes or less; or prepared ahead of time and stored, ready for a quick meal or snack
- EASY-CHEW: dishes for those who have problems with chewing
- HANDS-ON: foods that can be picked up and eaten without use of forks, knives, or spoons when there is difficulty with eating utensils
- BONE HEALTH: high calcium and/or magnesium, vitamins D and/or K for bone thinning/osteoporosis
- HEART HEALTH: low saturated fat/cholesterol; contains fish and/or nuts or is rich in vitamins E, B6, B12, folate, selenium
- HIGH FIBER: Contains at least 25 mg of fiber to help prevent constipation

Are these menus complete in all the recommended nutrients?

No, and I've noted this in the box marked "Concerns" on each menu. It's difficult to get 100% or more of all nutrients in a single day. However, eating a variety of different foods each day will help ensure that over a week's time, we do average enough of each nutrient.

Still, many experts advise that adults, especially older adults, take a multivitamin/mineral supplement daily, and I think this is a good idea. People with PD often have problems with cow's milk – for some folks, the protein in cow's milk blocks levodopa absorption more strongly than other proteins. Because milk is a major source of both calcium and vitamin D, this may mean that you'll need supplements of these.

Following is a listing of vitamins and minerals, in the amounts needed, per day, along with the Tolerable Upper Limit for each nutrient. Each age group has different nutrient requirements, so I've chosen amounts that are safe and adequate for adult men and women, particularly older adults. This does not include children, or women who are pregnant or lactating. Your doctor may advise larger amounts of some nutrients, for your individual needs.

Nutrients:	Goal Amount per day	Tolerable Upper Limit
Vitamin A	900 mcg	3000 mcg
Vitamin B1 (Thiamin)	1.2 mg	Not determined
Vitamin B2 (Riboflavin)	1.3 mg	Not determined
Vitamin B3 (Niacin)	16 mg	35 mg
Vitamin B6 (Pyridoxine)	1.7 mg	100 mg
Vitamin B12 (Cobalamin)	2.4 mcg	Not determined
Biotin	30 mcg	Not determined
Choline	550 mg	3500 mg
Folate	400 mcg	1000 mcg
Pantothenic acid	5 mg	Not determined
Vitamin C	90 mg	2000 mg
Vitamin D	15 mcg (400 IU)	50 mcg (2000 IU)
Vitamin E	15 mg	1000 mg
Vitamin K	120 mcg	Not determined
Calcium	1200 mg	2500 mg
Chromium	35 mcg	Not determined
Copper	900 mcg	10,000 mcg
*Iron	8 mg	45 mg
Magnesium	420 mg	**350 mg
Manganese	2.3 mg	11 mg
Phosphorus	700 mg	3000 mg
Selenium	55 mcg	400 mcg
Zinc	11 mg	40 mg

*Women age 19-50 require 18 mg iron daily
**350 mg obtained from supplements only; does not include intake from food and water

You'll notice that some menus combine *Cook Well* recipes with other foods, such as fruit juices, bread, crackers, coffee, and tea. Recipes in the cookbook are shown in normal typeface, other foods are shown in italics.

Use these to get started, then start putting together your own menus. And don't be afraid to use your own favorite family recipes as well!

Easy-Fix

"Easy-Fix" recipes in these menus don't require extensive slicing, chopping, or other complicated preparation; some, however, DO use long-cooking ingredients such as beans or rice, or granola, that can be prepared, then stored or frozen ahead of time. Thus they become "convenience foods."

Morning:
Easy Speedy Fruit-Filled Omelet (p. 38)
8 ounces calcium-fortified orange juice
Whole-wheat toast, butter, honey
Coffee or tea

Snack:
Berry Berry Frosty (p. 27)

Midday:
Split Pea & Barley Soup (p. 147)
2 rye crackers
Grape juice

Snack:
Curried Filberts (p. 20)

Evening:
Salmon Potato Cakes (p. 65)
Roasted Brussels Sprouts (p.114)
Whole wheat roll, butter
Glass of wine, juice, coffee or tea
Cinnamon Applesauce Squares (p. 187)

Nutrition information per day (approx.): 2038 calories, 269 g carbohydrates, 70 g protein, 73 g fat, 19 g saturated fat, 513 mg cholesterol, 1794 mg sodium, 47 g fiber.

Concerns: high in cholesterol; low in vitamins B12, D, E, calcium.

Notes:

Quick-Fix

Quick-Fix recipes can be prepared in about 45 minutes or less; or, in other cases, can be prepared ahead of time and stored, ready for a quick meal later. Great Granola, and Almond Cocoa Butter, are two examples.

Morning:
Great Granola (p. 50)
1/2 serving Orangey Banana Breakfast Shake (p. 29)

Midday:
Green Pea Soup (p. 157)
Blueberry & Tortellini Fruit Salad (p. 129)
Coffee, tea, or juice

Snack:
1/2 serving Tuna Tapenade (p. 17)

Evening:
Chicken a la Can (p. 90)
1/2 cup frozen broccoli, cooked according to package directions
Cran-Tea Cooler (p. 36)
Almond Cocoa Butter *(previously prepared and stored)*, **on a graham cracker (p. 184)**

Nutrition information per day (approx.): 2099 calories, 269 g carbohydrates, 84 g protein, 84 g fat, 15 g saturated fat, 193 mg cholesterol, 1768 mg sodium, 33 g fiber.

Concerns: Low in vitamins D, K, biotin

Notes: _____

_____

_____

_____

_____

_____

Easy-Chew

Easy-Chew foods don't require extensive chewing. However, easy-chew does *not* necessarily mean a food is easy to swallow. Persons with dysphagia (swallowing problems, or choking) should see a speech pathologist, to determine whether there is risk for choking, or aspiration pneumonia. Ask your doctor for a referral.

Morning:
Breakfast Egg-Spinach Bake (p. 40)
8 ounces calcium-fortified orange juice
Coffee or tea

Snack:
Strawberry-Banana Smoothie (p. 30)

Midday:
Gazpacho (p. 158)
Burgers Dijon (P. 93)
½ cup noodles tossed with butter
Coffee, tea or iced tea

Snack:
Honey Fig Bars (p. 186)
Fruit juice

Evening:
Navy Bean-Tomato Gratin (p. 52)
Gingered Fruit (p. 131)
Honey of a Carrot Cake (p. 182)
Coffee, tea or iced tea

Nutrition information per day (approx.): 2161 calories, 318 g carbohydrates, 78 g protein, 74 g fat, 25 g saturated fat, 616 mg cholesterol, 2331 mg sodium, 35 g fiber.

Concerns: High in cholesterol; low in vitamin D

Notes: _____

_____

_____

_____

Hands-On

Hands-On foods can be picked up and eaten with the hands, or sipped from a mug; they don't require use of eating utensils such as fork, knife, or spoon.

Morning:
**Banana-Oat Pancakes,
rolled up,
and dunked in a bowl of maple
syrup (p. 46)**
4 ounces grape juice
Coffee or tea

Snack:
**Rainy Day Tomato Snack
(p. 12)**

Midday:
*Tuna salad sandwich on whole
wheat bread (your favorite recipe)*
Carrot and celery sticks
Green Tea Sipper (p. 34)

Snack:
**Eastern Fruit Smoothie
(p. 31)**

Evening:
**Pat Garcia's Meatballs Two
Ways
(p. 96)
Autumn Pumpkin Soup,
sipped from a mug (p. 156)**
Whole-wheat crackers
Coffee or tea

Nutrition information per day (approx): 2205 calories, 325 g carbohydrates, 84 g protein, 68 g fat, 16 g saturated fat, 161 mg cholesterol, 2211 mg sodium, 20 g fiber.

<u>*Concerns*</u>: **May be too low in fiber for those with constipation; 25 - 35 grams is advisable. Low in folate, pantothenic acid, biotin, vitamin D, vitamin K, calcium**

Notes: _____

_____

_____

_____

Bone Health

Recipes marked "Bone Health" contain at contain at least 10% of the RDA for two or more of the following: calcium, magnesium, phosphorus, vitamin D, and/or vitamin K – but not necessarily *all four* of these vital, bone-protecting nutrients. If you have been diagnosed with osteoporosis, you will most likely need to take supplements of calcium and vitamin D, and possibly magnesium (see "Concerns" below). Ask your doctor for a referral to a registered dietitian, who can help you plan sufficient intake of these important nutrients. *(Note: this day's menu contains 1637 mg calcium, 355 mg magnesium, and 244 mcg vitamin K; but, only 3 mcg of vitamin D, about 29% of the RDA for older adults.)*

Morning:
Broccoli Breakfast Casseroles (p. 41)
1 cup applesauce
8 ounces Calcium-fortified orange juice
Tea

Snack:
Strawberry-Banana Smoothie (p. 30)

Midday:
Manhattan Clam and Potato Chowder (p. 143)
Whole wheat crackers
Hot or iced tea

Snack:
4 ounces plain yogurt with 1/2 cup sliced fruit of your choice

Evening:
Kathrynne's Tostada (p. 56)
Easy Apple Dessert Casserole (p. 188)
Hot or iced tea

Nutrition information per day (approx): 2009 calories, 318 g carbohydrates, 80 g protein, 60 g fat, 21g saturated fat, 368 mg cholesterol, 2279 mg sodium, 50 g fiber.

Concerns: High in cholesterol; low in vitamins D, E

Notes:

_____

_____

_____

Heart Health

To protect the heart, select recipes rich in vitamins B6, B12, folate, E, selenium, potassium, nuts, soy, fish, tea, and soluble fiber (oats, soy, legumes). Moderate your use of foods high in saturated fat and cholesterol. Here are some recipes and suggestions that can help.

Morning:
1/2 serving Baked Cinnamon-Raisin Oatmeal (p. 44)
8 ounces grape juice
Black or green tea

Snack:
Spicy Fruit and Nuts (p. 23)

Midday:
Tuscan Bean Soup (p. 153)
1 Raisin Bran Muffin, 1 teaspoon butter (p. 178)
Green Tea Ginger Sparkler (p. 35)

Snack:
1/2 serving No-Fork Salad (p. 18)

Evening:
Salmon Bake With Pecan Crunch Coating (p. 67)
Quinoa Salad (p. 111)
Asparagus Dijon (p. 124)
1/2 serving Honey Lime Pears (p. 189)
Glass of wine, or green or black tea

Nutrition information per day (approx): 2000 calories, 256 g carbohydrates, 66 g protein, 77 g fat, 17 g saturated fat, 167 mg cholesterol, 1697 mg sodium, 32 g fiber.

Concerns: Low in vitamin D, calcium

Notes: _____

_____

_____

_____

_____

High Fiber

Constipation can be a problem, due to PD (See *Eat Well, Stay Well with Parkinson's Disease*; and audiocassette *Parkinson's Disease and Constipation*); and it's often aggravated by the medications used to treat PD. Insoluble fiber, found in whole grains, legumes, vegetables, fruits, and nuts, along with plenty of fluids, will help to combat constipation. The fiber particles soak up water, making the stool soft and bulky. Aim for at least 25, and up to 40, grams of fiber daily, along with 6 to 8 eight-ounce glasses of water per day.

Upon arising:
8-ounce glass of water

Morning:
8-ounce glass of water
Orange-Blueberry Whole Wheat Griddle Cakes, Maple Syrup, Butter (p. 45)
Coffee or tea
8 ounces calcium-fortified orange juice

Snack:
8-ounce glass of water
2 Raisin Bran Muffins (p. 178)

Midday:
8-ounce glass of water
Lentil Salad with Spinach (p. 165)
Coffee or tea

Snack:
8-ounce glass of water
Glazed Walnuts (p. 21)

Evening:
8-ounce glass of water
Crockery Turkey Wing Dinner (p. 86)
Glass of wine, or juice
Coffee or tea

2 hours before bed:
8-ounce glass of water

Nutrition information per day (approx.): 2125 calories, 312 g carbohydrates, 77 g protein, 60 g fat, 12 g saturated fat, 215 mg cholesterol, 1653 mg sodium, 51 g fiber.

Concerns: Low in vitamin B12, D, calcium

Notes: _____

_____

_____

Weight Gain Plan

Unplanned or unwanted weight loss can sometimes occur as PD advances. This can occur for a variety of reasons (see *Eat Well, Stay Well With Parkinson's Disease*) and it can lead to malnutrition. It may be helpful to eat many small meals or nutritious snacks throughout the day, rather than three large meals; cooking dishes that can be divided into small portions and frozen is a great help. Consider using fortified foods, such as calcium-fortified orange juice, and fortified breakfast cereals, for extra nutrients. Also, ginger can sometimes stimulate the appetite. Here's a sample plan to try.

Snack:
Fresh Ginger Tea (p. 32)
One-half serving Orangey Banana Breakfast Shake (p. 29)

Morning:
One-half serving Breakfast Egg-Spinach Bake (p. 40)
4 ounces calcium-fortified orange juice
Fresh Ginger Tea (p. 32)

Snack:
One-half serving Orangey Banana Breakfast Shake (p. 29)

Snack:
One-half serving Gingered Fruit (P. 131)
1 slice whole-grain toast with butter and jelly

Midday:
One-half serving Cashew Rice (p. 105)
One-half serving Navy Bean-Tomato Gratin (p. 52)
4 ounces skim or 1% milk

Snack:
Spicy Fruit and Nuts (P. 23)
Green Tea Sipper (p. 34)

Snack:
Rainy Day Tomato Snack (p. 12)

Evening:
One-half serving Sweet Potatoes and Apples (p. 118)
Basic Best Salmon Loaf (p. 70)
Fresh Ginger Tea (p. 32)

Snack:
Honey Pecan Snack Spread (p. 183)
Graham cracker
4 ounces fruit juice

Nutrition information per day (approx.): 1981 calories, 289 g carbohydrates, 82 g protein, 62 g fat, 23 g saturated fat, 425 mg cholesterol, 2604 mg sodium, 29 g fiber.

<u>*Concerns*</u>: **Low in vitamin E; high in cholesterol**

Lowered Protein Plan

As PD advances, it can become more difficult to get the best possible absorption of levodopa (see *Eat Well, Stay Well with Parkinson's Disease*). This may be due to slowed stomach emptying or frequent constipation; it may also be due to the increasing reliance upon levodopa as the dopamine-producing neurons in the brain continue to die off.

Because protein can block the absorption of levodopa, many people find that eating less protein can lead to better levodopa assimilation. The concern is to be sure to get _enough_ protein to meet your body's needs. People with PD need about 1/2 gram of protein per pound of body weight. So, for example, a person who weighs 150 pounds should aim for about 75 grams of protein per day.

This amount of protein should be divided about equally among three meals: breakfast, midday, and evening. Levodopa should be taken about 30 to 60 minutes before these meals. In-between meal snacks should be very low in protein, so as not to block any levodopa used during the day. The recipes given here, as well as many modern recipes, list the grams of protein per serving. Also, here is a list of the approximate amounts of protein in some common foods.

Amounts of protein in common foods	
Food	Grams Protein (approximate)
Bread, 1 slice	3
Meat, poultry, fish, 1 ounce	7
Vegetables, 1/2 cup	2
Fruit, 1/2 cup	0
Milk, 8 ounces	8
Yogurt, 8 ounces	9
Egg, large	6
Cheese, 1 ounce	7
Cooked dried beans, 1 cup	20
Nuts, 4 tablespoons (1 ounce)	4
1 tablespoon peanut butter	4

Lowered Protein Menu

Here is an example one-day menu, designed for a 150-pound person. Determine your protein needs by multiplying your weight in pounds times 0.5 (grams protein), and adjust serving sizes accordingly.

Morning:
Crustless Quiche (p. 39)
8 ounces calcium-fortified
orange juice
1 slice whole-grain toast, butter,
jelly
Coffee, tea, or iced tea
(about 24 grams protein)

Snack:
Gingered Fruit (p. 133)
(about 1 gram protein)

Midday:
Double Decker Pasta Salad
(p. 162)
Two rye crackers
Low sodium tomato juice
(about 23 grams protein)

Snack:
1 banana
6 oz grape juice
(0 grams protein)

Evening:
Pat Garcia's Meatballs Two
Ways with 1 cup cooked
spaghetti (p. 96)
Broccoli with Oil and Garlic
(p. 113)
Fruit juice, coffee, tea, or iced tea
(about 24 grams protein)

Nutrition information per day (approx.): 2188 calories, 353 g carbohydrates, 72 g protein, 55 g fat, 19 g saturated fat, 550 mg cholesterol, 1975 mg sodium, 32 g fiber.

<u>*Concerns*</u>: High in cholesterol; low in vit. D, magnesium

REFERENCES

1. Galli RL, Shukitt-Hale B, Youdim KA, Joseph JA. Fruit polyphenolics and brain aging: nutritional interventions targeting age-related neuronal and behavioral deficits. Ann N Y Acad Sci 2002 Apr;959:128-3

2. Seeram NP, Momin RA, Nair MG, Bourquin LD. Cyclooxygenase inhibitory and antioxidant cyanidin glycosides in cherries and berries. Phytomedicine 2001 Sep;8(5):362-9.

3. Yan X, Murphy BT, Hammond GB, Vinson JA, Neto CC. Antioxidant activities and antitumor screening of extracts from cranberry fruit (Vaccinium macrocarpon). J Agric Food Chem 2002 Oct 9;50(21):5844-9.

4. Tanskanen A, Hibbeln JR, Tuomilehto J, Uutela A, Haukkala A, Viinamaki H, Lehtonen J, Vartiainen E. Fish consumption and depressive symptoms in the general population in Finland. Psychiatr Serv 2001 Apr;52(4):529-31.

5. Severus WE, Littman AB, Stoll AL. Omega-3 fatty acids, homocysteine, and the increased risk of cardiovascular mortality in major depressive disorder. Harv Rev Psychiatry 2001 Nov-Dec;9(6):280-93.

6. Peet M, Horrobin DF. A dose-ranging study of the effects of ethyl-eicosapentaenoate in patients with ongoing depression despite apparently adequate treatment with standard drugs. Arch Gen Psychiatry 2002 Oct;59(10):913-9

7. Tarpila S, Kivinen A. Ground flaxseed is an effective hypolipidemic bulk laxative. Gastroenterology. 1997;112:A836.

8. Lucas EA, Wild RD, Hammond LJ, Khalil DA, Juma S, Daggy BP, Stoecker BJ, Arjmandi BH. Flaxseed improves lipid profile without altering biomarkers of bone metabolism in postmenopausal women. J Clin Endocrinol Metab 2002 Apr;87(4):1527-32.

9. Demark-Wahnefried W, Price DT, Polascik TJ, Robertson CN, Anderson EE, Paulson DF, Walther PJ, Gannon M, Vollmer RT. Pilot study of dietary fat restriction and flaxseed supplementation in men with prostate cancer before surgery: exploring the effects on hormonal levels, prostate-specific antigen, and histopathologic features. Urology 2001 Jul;58(1):47-52.

10. Haggans CJ, Hutchins AM, Olson BA, Thomas W, Martini MC, Slavin JL. Effect of flaxseed consumption on urinary estrogen metabolites in postmenopausal women. Nutr Cancer 1999;33(2):188-95.

11. Physicians Desk Reference for Herbal Medicines. Medical Economics Company, Inc. Montvale NJ 07645-1742, 1998.

12. O'Byrne, Dawn J, et al. Comparison of the antioxidant effects of Concord grape juice flavonoids and á-tocopherol on markers of oxidative stress in healthy adults. Am J Clin Nutr 2002;76:1367-74.

13. Rimando AM, Cuendet M, Desmarchelier C, Mehta RG, Pezzuto JM, Duke SO. Cancer chemopreventive and antioxidant activities of pterostilbene, a naturally occurring analogue of resveratrol. J Agric Food Chem 2002 Jun 5;50(12):3453-7.

14. Gheldof N, Engeseth NJ. Antioxidant capacity of honeys from various floral sources based on the determination of oxygen radical absorbance capacity and inhibition of in vitro lipoprotein oxidation in human serum samples. J Agric Food Chem 2002 May 8;50(10):3050-5

15. Zhang SM, Hernan MA, Chen H, Spiegelman D, Willett WC, Ascherio A. Intakes of vitamins E and C, carotenoids, vitamin supplements, and PD risk. Neurology 2002 Oct 22;59(8):1161-9.

16. Anderson RA, Polansky MM. Tea enhances insulin activity. J Agric Food Chem 2002 Nov 20;50(24):7182-6.

17. Hirano R, Momiyama Y, Takahashi R, Taniguchi H, Kondo K, Nakamura H, Ohsuzu F. Comparison of green tea intake in Japanese patients with and without angiographic coronary artery disease. Am J Cardiol 2002 Nov 15;90(10):1150-3

18. Wu CH, Yang YC, Yao WJ, Lu FH, Wu JS, Chang CJ. Epidemiological evidence of increased bone mineral density in habitual tea drinkers. Arch Intern Med 2002 May 13;162(9):1001-6

19. Choi JY, Park CS, Kim DJ, Cho MH, Jin BK, Pie JE, Chung WG. Prevention of nitric oxide-mediated 1-methyl-4-phenyl-1,2,3,6-tetrahydropyridine-induced Parkinson's disease in mice by tea phenolic epigallocatechin 3-gallate. Neurotoxicology 2002 Sep;23(3):367-74.

20. Gescher AJ, Sharma RA, Steward WP. Cancer chemoprevention by dietary constituents: a tale of failure and promise. Lancet Oncol 2001 Jun;2(6):371-9.

21. Arun N, Nalini N. Efficacy of turmeric on blood sugar and polyol pathway in diabetic albino rats. Plant Foods Hum Nutr 2002 Winter;57(1):41-52.

22. Wegener T. The status of herbal antilipemic agents. Wien Med Wochenschr 2002;152 (15-16):412-7 .

23. Phan TT, See P, Lee ST, Chan SY. Protective effects of curcumin against oxidative damage on skin cells in vitro: its implication for wound healing. J Trauma 2001 Nov;51(5):927-31.

24. Lim GP, Chu T, Yang F, Beech W, Frautschy SA, Cole GM. The curry spice curcumin reduces oxidative damage and amyloid pathology in an Alzheimer transgenic mouse. J Neurosci 2001 Nov 1;21(21):8370-7.

25. Kim DS, Park SY, Kim JK. Curcuminoids from Curcuma longa L. (Zingiberaceae) that protect PC12 rat pheochromocytoma and normal human umbilical vein endothelial cells from betaA(1-42) insult. Neurosci Lett 2001 Apr 27;303(1):57-61.

26. Vesper J, Klostermann F, Stockhammer F, Funk T, Brock M. Results of chronic subthalamic nucleus stimulation for Parkinson's disease: a 1-year follow-up study. Surg Neurol 2002 May;57(5):306-11; discussion 311-3.

27. Bejjani BP, Gervais D, Arnulf I, Papadopoulos S, Demeret S, Bonnet AM, Cornu P, Damier P, Agid Y. Axial parkinsonian symptoms can be improved: the role of levodopa and bilateral subthalamic stimulation. J Neurol Neurosurg Psychiatry 2000 May;68(5):595-600.

28. Xie J, Krack P, Benabid AL, Pollak P. Effect of bilateral subthalamic nucleus stimulation on parkinsonian gait. J Neurol 2001 Dec;248(12):1068-72.

29. Spottke EA, Volkmann J, Lorenz D, Krack P, Smala AM, Sturm V, Gerstner A, Berger K, Hellwig D, Deuschl G, Freund HJ, Oertel WH, Dodel RC. Evaluation of healthcare utilization and health status of patients with Parkinson's disease treated with deep brain stimulation of the subthalamic nucleus. J Neurol 2002 Jun;249(6):759-66.

30. Martinez-Martin P, Valldeoriola F, Tolosa E, Pilleri M, Molinuevo JL, Rumia J, Ferrer E. Bilateral subthalamic nucleus stimulation and quality of life in advanced Parkinson's disease. Mov Disord 2002 Mar;17(2):372-7.

31. Ostergaard K, Sunde N, Dupont E. Effects of bilateral stimulation of the subthalamic nucleus in patients with severe Parkinson's disease and motor fluctuations. Mov Disord 2002 Jul;17(4):693-700.

32. Moro E, Scerrati M, Romito LM, Roselli R, Tonali P, Albanese A. Chronic subthalamic nucleus stimulation reduces medication requirements in Parkinson's disease. Neurology 1999 Jul 13;53(1):85-90.

33. Valldeoriola F, Pilleri M, Tolosa E, Molinuevo JL, Rumia J, Ferrer E. Bilateral subthalamic stimulation monotherapy in advanced Parkinson's disease: long-term follow-up of patients. Mov Disord 2002 Jan;17(1):125-32.

34. Delgado-Rodriguez M, Medina-Cuadros M, Gomez-Ortega A, Martinez-Gallego G, Mariscal-Ortiz M, Martinez-Gonzalez MA, Sillero-Arenas M. Cholesterol and serum albumin levels as predictors of cross infection, death, and length of hospital stay. Arch Surg 2002 Jul;137(7):805-12.

35. Edington J, Boorman J, Durrant ER, Perkins A, Giffin CV, James R, Thomson JM, Oldroyd JC, Smith JC, Torrance AD, Blackshaw V, Green S, Hill CJ, Berry C, McKenzie C, Vicca N, Ward JE, Coles SJ. Prevalence of malnutrition on admission to four hospitals in England. The Malnutrition Prevalence Group. Clin Nutr 2000 Jun;19(3):191-5.

36. Chima CS, Barco K, Dewitt ML, Maeda M, Teran JC, Mullen KD. Relationship of nutritional status to length of stay, hospital costs, and discharge status of patients hospitalized in the medicine service. J Am Diet Assoc 1997 Sep;97(9):975-8; quiz 979-80.

37. Gironell A, Pascual-Sedano B, Otermin P, Kulisevsky J. Weight gain after functional surgery for Parkinsons disease. Neurologia 2002 Jun-Jul;17(6):310-6.

Ask the Parkinson Dietitian

Do you have questions about diet or nutrition for Parkinson's Disease?
E-mail the Parkinson Dietitian!

It's now possible for people with Parkinson's, their family members, Support Group Leaders, and health professionals, to ask questions about nutrition for PD, and receive a personal answer.

The National Parkinson Foundation has provided an online discussion forum called *Ask the Parkinson Dietitian*. This service is provided by a grant, so that people who might not have access to a dietitian experienced in Parkinson's disease can now get nutrition help.

If you would like to ask a question, go to:

http://www.parkinson.org/

Locate "Ask the Parkinson Dietitian" and follow the instructions, then post your question. You can also use a search box to find previous questions and answers on many topics, and some short articles herbs, supplements, and other topics that are pertinent for those with PD.

I hope to hear from you on "Ask the Parkinson Dietitian." Please pass this information on to support groups, hospitals, and health organizations in your area.

Sincerely,

Kathrynne Holden, MS, RD

Nutrition You Can Live With!

A Series of Diet Resources for Parkinson's Disease

For people with PD, their families, PD support groups, and health professionals: the *Nutrition You Can Live With* series, by Kathrynne Holden, MS, RD, is a <u>must</u> for maintaining optimal nutritional health. For information, including prices and ordering details:

Tel: 877-565-2665 or 970-224-5066; Fax: 970-407-7755

E-mail: Sonja Johnston <sonjaj@1stclassdirect.com>

http://www.nutritionucanlivewith.com

Eat Well, Stay Well with Parkinson's Disease

Explains the nutritional hurdles that occur with PD and provides practical ways to overcome these hurdles and maintain good health. Topics include:

★ Protein and levodopa; timing meals and levodopa; recipes and menus

★ Controlling constipation; preventing bowel impaction

★ Dehydration – the importance of fluids

★ Bone health

★ The role of B vitamins

★ Dealing with heartburn, reflux, ulcers, hiatal hernia

★ Unplanned weight loss – why it happens, how to prevent it

★ Chewing and swallowing concerns

Cook Well, Stay Well with Parkinson's Disease

First-ever cookbook for those with PD! Lists *SuperFoods* – those with nutrients of special importance in PD.

★ Includes recipes for breakfast, snacks, beverages, main dishes, side dishes, soups, salads, sandwiches, breads, and desserts.

★ Also includes one-day menu templates that demonstrate how to use the recipes for conditions, such as constipation, chewing difficulties, etc.

Parkinson's Disease and Constipation:

Audiocassette and Guidebook

Written and read by Kathrynne Holden, MS, RD

This tape-and-booklet set is designed to suit the needs of both individuals and PD support groups. Answers many important questions:

★ Why constipation occurs with PD; its consequences

★ Controlling constipation naturally

★ Tracking fiber and fluids

★ Easy ways to increase fiber

The audiocassette can be played by itself, and is particularly helpful for those with vision problems or other reading difficulties. The guidebook contains the text of the audiocassette, a form for tracking fiber and fluid intake, a list of fiber sources, and a guide for group use of the tape by PD support groups.

Parkinson's Disease: Guidelines for Medical Nutrition Therapy
A manual for health professionals
Kathrynne Holden, MS, RD

An annual subscription to this manual includes a three-ring binder containing state-of-the-art guidelines for the health professional working with people who have Parkinson's. You'll also receive twice-yearly updates and/or new sections to the manual, as new information becomes available. Contains the only available information on nutrition support for patients using levodopa; and a unique section on PD medications and their nutritional implications.

The manual contains unique PD-specific assessment tools:

★ FOOD/MEDICATION DIARY with guidelines for its use;
★ INITIAL INTERVIEW FORM, with explanatory patient handout

Use these to provide medical nutrition therapy for concerns related to PD medications and disease effects. Tabbed sections include explanatory text and guidelines for major nutrition-related concerns:

★ protein-levodopa interactions
★ PD medications and their impact on nutrition
★ gastroparesis
★ osteopenia/osteoporosis
★ dehydration
★ constipation / fecal impaction
★ unplanned weight loss
★ enteral feeding

and many more. Includes reproducible patient education handouts.

For information, including prices and ordering details:

Five Star Living, Inc.
760 S.E. Frontage Road
Fort Collins CO 80524
Tel: 877-565-2665 or 970-224-5066; Fax: 970-407-7755
E-mail: Sonja Johnston <sonjaj@1stclassdirect.com>
http://www.nutritionucanlivewith.com